6
08C

Agricultural Bioterrorism: A Federal Strategy to Meet the Threat

Henry S. Parker

McNair Paper 65

D1157344

INSTITUTE FOR NATIONAL STRATEGIC STUDIES

NATIONAL DEFENSE UNIVERSITY

WASHINGTON, D.C.

2002

C.1

The opinions, conclusions, and recommendations expressed or implied within are those of the contributors and do not necessarily reflect the views of the Department of Defense or any other department or agency of the Federal Government. This publication is cleared for public release; distribution unlimited.

Portions of this work may be quoted or reprinted without further permission, with credit to the Institute for National Strategic Studies. A courtesy copy of any reviews and tearsheets would be appreciated.

HV
6432
.P37
2002

Second printing with revisions, June 2003
First printing, March 2002

For sale by the U.S. Government Printing Office. To order, contact
Superintendent of Documents, Mail Stop: SSOP, Washington, D.C. 20402–9328
(ISSN 1071–7552)

Contents

Foreword

The astonishing specter of September 11, 2001, jarred America and, indeed, all free nations, into accepting the previously unthinkable—the world's only remaining superpower is vulnerable to catastrophic attack and asymmetric warfare, even within its own borders. In a few short hours Americans came to realize that, for a fanatical, resourceful, and patient enemy, there are neither ethical bounds nor societal mores to delineate the nature of the target, the weapon of choice, or the scale of the violence. To put it another way, for these enemies there are no rules of engagement and there is no honor.

Since September 11, our national sense of vulnerability has steadily risen. We have been in a near-constant state of high alert because of credible threats to our Nation's nuclear installations, power plants, transportation nodes, and other critical national infrastructures. We know that at least nine countries support offensive terrorism programs, and that Al Qaeda—Osama bin Laden's international terrorist organization—has been committed to developing and deploying weapons of mass destruction against U.S. targets. And the possibility that the recent anthrax attacks were perpetrated by a domestic terrorist with access to a Federal Government, academic, or private laboratory that possessed anthrax for legitimate scientific reasons has brought fear to the doorsteps of virtually every home, business, and public institution in the country.

We are now also facing up to a less publicized, but potentially devastating threat—terrorism directed against the Nation's food and agricultural infrastructure. As this paper elucidates, American farms, food, and agriculture systems are exceedingly vulnerable to deliberate disruption by hostile interests intent on undermining confidence in food supplies or wreaking havoc on the agricultural sector of the American economy, which accounts for one-sixth of our gross domestic product.

Because of its breadth, diversity, and unparalleled success, U.S. agriculture is an inviting target for terrorists. Not only are food supplies vital for feeding our own population and others around the world, and important for the Nation's economic health, but American agriculture is a vivid example of the capabilities of modern scientific farming. Intelligence reports indicate that a number of countries have active research programs that could produce biological agents to threaten crops and livestock.

Naturally occurring outbreaks of diseases signal the devastation that could result from a carefully choreographed intentional release. Thus the recent Foot and mouth disease epidemics in Taiwan and Great Britain, or hog cholera in the Netherlands, or the infection of Florida citrus trees with citrus canker, aptly demonstrate the vulnerability of living targets to biological pathogens and the economic chaos that can result from an outbreak—intentional or otherwise.

Floyd P. Horn
Director for Food, Agriculture, and Water Security
Office of Homeland Security
Executive Office of the President

Acknowledgments

Many individuals and organizations supported, encouraged, and assisted in the research that led to this paper. I am grateful to the U.S. Department of Agriculture and the Agricultural Research Service (ARS) for the opportunity to attend the Industrial College of the Armed Forces (ICAF), where this research was conducted. I particularly appreciate the support and encouragement of Floyd Horn, ARS Administrator, and Caird Rexroad, ARS Associate Deputy Administrator for Animal Production, Product Value, and Safety. I am also grateful to Lew Smith for assuming my duties on the ARS National Program Staff while I was on assignment at ICAF.

I benefited from the expertise of a number of authorities in the public and private sectors. In particular, Norm Steele of ARS freely shared his extensive knowledge of agricultural biotechnology and bioterrorism issues, suggested valuable contacts, and reviewed drafts of the report manuscript thoroughly. I appreciate the perspective, suggestions, and time of Michael Goldblatt of the Defense Advanced Research Projects Agency and Randall Murch of the Defense Threat Reduction Agency. I am also obliged to Terry Wilson of the Animal and Plant Health Inspection Service at the U.S. Department of Agriculture for his encouragement, time, information, and draft manuscript on agricultural bioterrorism.

I am indebted to many individuals at ICAF for their support and assistance. The ICAF program successfully combines strong scholarship, professional and personal development, and fun—a combination often aspired to but seldom achieved. I appreciate the leadership of the ICAF Commandant, Major General Richard Engel, USAF, during my tenure in the program. My research advisor, Joseph Goldberg, was always accessible and helpful, providing sound advice for the original research proposal, scrupulously reviewing and offering valuable suggestions on report drafts, facilitating interactions with experts, and generously sharing his wealth of knowledge. I am also grateful to my principal faculty advisor, Richard Shivar, for his support, encouragement, and insights into the Federal emergency management structure. Seth Carus of the Center for Counterproliferation Research at the National Defense University, a recognized authority on terrorism, and Gregory Foster of ICAF served on my research committee. Their expertise and suggestions were invaluable. Colonel James Toth, USMC (Ret.), was an unofficial mentor throughout my ICAF program. I appreciate his encouragement and support.

I also wish to acknowledge the contributions of Stephen Flanagan, Director of the Institute for National Strategic Studies at National Defense University (NDU). Dr. Flanagan's unflagging support from the outset of this project was instrumental in bringing it to fruition. Thanks are also due to the staff of NDU Press—General Editor William Bode, and editors George Maerz, Lisa Yambrick, and Jeffrey Smotherman—who turned the manuscript into a polished publication under the supervision of Robert Silano, Director of Publications.

Finally, and most importantly, I am deeply grateful to my wife, Susan, and our sons, James and John, for their support and patience. They suffered through innumerable readings of draft sections and somehow managed to convey both genuine interest and helpful suggestions.

Introduction

The attacks of September 11, 2001, have made Americans acutely aware of their vulnerability to terrorism. Now the Nation is focused on improving defensive measures and rooting out and destroying the global infrastructure of terrorism. In response to the terrorist offensive, the Bush administration has engineered an international coalition against terrorism; dedicated substantial new resources to prevent or deter this blight; undertaken military action against blatant practitioners of terrorism; and established a new Office of Homeland Security, under the leadership of former Pennsylvania governor Tom Ridge, to coordinate the Federal response to terrorism.

As America prepares defenses against catastrophes barely conceivable only a few months ago, the threat of bioterrorism in particular looms larger than ever. Fears of anthrax, smallpox, and plague pervade the American consciousness, fueled by reports that some of the plane hijackers involved in the World Trade Center and Pentagon attacks had specific interest in crop duster aircraft that could be used to disseminate aerosols of pathogens. Because of this, the Nation is stepping up its defenses against bioterrorism.

Nevertheless, little attention has been given to agricultural biowarfare and bioterrorism or to the roles and responsibilities of the public and private sectors in deterring and responding to potential attacks. Few Americans appreciate the gravity of the threat of bioterrorist attacks against the American food and agriculture infrastructure. This point is exemplified in a General Accounting Office (GAO) report on combating terrorism released 9 days after the attacks of September 11.[1] The report did not address threats to American agriculture, nor did it involve participation by the U.S. Department of Agriculture (USDA). It focused only on terrorism directed against "civilian targets"; therefore, according to GAO, it "did not focus on terrorism directed against agricultural targets." GAO explained that agriculture was not included in the review because it has not been designated a critical national infrastructure.

But agriculture *is* a critical American infrastructure. It constitutes one-sixth of gross domestic product (GDP)—over a trillion dollars a year. The food and agriculture sector is the Nation's largest employer; one of eight Americans works in an occupation directly supported by food production. Agriculture exports total over $50 billion annually, making the farm sector the largest positive contributor to the national trade balance. The farming system is the most productive and efficient in the world, enabling Americans to spend less than 11 percent of disposable income on food, compared to a global average of 20 to 30 percent.

Officials are beginning to recognize that this vast network of food and fiber production, processing, distribution, and sales is a potential—even inevitable—target of hostile interests employing biological agents for political, economic, or criminal objectives. Even the threat of attack could jeopardize consumer confidence, disrupt commodity markets, and wreak economic havoc.

American agriculture is often concentrated, highly accessible, vertically integrated, and of limited genetic diversity; historically it has been free of major disease outbreaks, so vaccines are not routinely used. Consequently, pathogens could be introduced easily and spread rapidly. Widespread use of antibiotics in livestock production makes U.S. animals vulnerable to antibiotic-resistant bacteria. Advances in genetic engineering have raised the prospect of transgenic pathogens and pests that are resistant to conventional control methods. In addition, it may be hard to distinguish a biological attack from a natural disease outbreak. Signs of infections may be manifested slowly, delaying effective response by authorities. Finally, attacks against agriculture may be less risky to perpetrators than attacks against humans because many anti-agriculture pathogens are comparatively safe to work with. Also, public reaction may be less intense because humans are not being directly targeted (unless the goal is food contamination), and there is currently no national policy prescribing criminal penalties for biological attacks against targets other than humans.

The Federal Government is beginning to respond to the emerging threat of agricultural biowarfare and bioterrorism. Federal intelligence agencies, in cooperation with USDA, are defining the extent of the threat and briefing key Government officials. Federal research agencies, led by USDA, are mobilizing resources and developing research plans to detect and identify, epidemiologically map, and control deliberately introduced pathogens and pests. Agriculture and food safety are now included in a National Security Council (NSC) framework for preparedness against weapons of mass destruction. Yet, despite these initiatives, the Nation is poorly prepared to prevent and respond to attacks on its food and agriculture infrastructure. The Federal Government must act quickly and decisively to protect food and agriculture systems. If we fail to act, the consequences could be far more damaging and long lasting than a direct and more visible terrorist attack against people.

To combat this threat, it is critical that the Federal Government, state and local governments, and the agribusiness sector clearly identify mutual roles and responsibilities and develop a coordinated strategy to address the threat. USDA should lead the development of this strategy.

To assure readiness, USDA should provide Federal leadership with a coordinated, stand-alone, interagency strategy and program to combat agricultural biowarfare and bioterrorism. Stand-alone attention and USDA leadership are both desirable and justified because the department has overall Federal responsibility for food safety and security and a broad range of programs and capabilities to deter and respond to threats against food and agriculture. It also has connections with the grassroots interests and the national agribusiness spectrum through an extensive network of field offices, agricultural extension specialists, research facilities, and land-grant universities in virtually every American county. In fact, USDA may be unique among Federal agencies in the closeness of its ties to constituencies. If subsumed into larger Federal programs, agricultural concerns could be buried in the enormously complex national security and counterterrorism bureaucracy, where it would be overshadowed by human health issues, cyberterrorism, and more conventional threats.

However, stand-alone attention should not be construed as acting in a vacuum. A national program to protect food and agriculture must be *strongly* linked to other national security and counterterrorism programs through the NSC structure and should involve strategic partnerships with other Federal, state, and local agencies and nongovernmental organizations—all of which have programs and capabilities that can contribute to the agriculture program—and with the private sector. Key objectives of a national strategy should be to:

- establish clear, well-coordinated Federal interagency mechanisms for gathering, assessing, and sharing sensitive intelligence information about hostile threats to U.S. food and agriculture

- increase significantly Federal research capabilities related to animal or plant health, food safety, and agricultural biowarfare and bioterrorism
- expand Federal staff in key areas
- create well-coordinated interagency mechanisms among USDA, the Federal Bureau of Investigation, and the Department of Defense for collaborative forensics investigations
- identify and include elements of other Federal terrorism and bioterrorism strategies that are applicable to countering agricultural bioterrorism
- expand and strategically site national supplies of critical vaccines and pharmaceuticals to protect against and treat the agricultural diseases most likely to be launched by terrorists
- establish a nationwide electronic communications and data management network that links the private agribusiness community with emergency management staff, field response personnel, and key Federal, state, and local agencies
- develop and implement a national emergency disease response plan for food and agriculture
- establish clear roles, responsibilities, expectations, and performance measures, as well as coordination mechanisms, for Federal, state, and local public and private organizations and interests
- identify feasible options for providing financial assistance to agribusiness interests impacted by biological attacks
- develop and implement professional and public education programs
- improve international cooperation to deter and respond to agricultural biowarfare and bioterrorism.

This paper reviews the nature and threat of agricultural bioterrorism, examines present national capabilities and plans to meet the threat, and proposes a USDA-led Federal strategy, including partnerships with key public and private organizations, that could strengthen American ability to prevent, respond to, and remediate biological attacks against national food and agriculture infrastructures. This paper focuses particularly on agricultural *bioterrorism*; however, a scenario of agricultural *biowarfare*, carried out by hostile nations, or a criminal action (*biocrime*), is at least as plausible as an act of terrorism, and a strategy to deter and respond to agricultural bioterrorism would apply equally to biowarfare and biocrime.

Chapter One

Bioterrorism, Biowarfare, and National Security

The United States faces a host of threats to its national security from diverse, nontraditional, unpredictable, and potentially covert sources. Of special concern are hostile nations or special interest groups that represent a spectrum of causes from religious fundamentalism to extreme environmentalism and threaten a wide range of military and civilian targets. These interests are likely to use weapons of mass destruction to achieve their goals, employing tools and technologies that are not only powerful but also difficult to detect or deter. A resourceful enemy bent on a destructive mission has potential access to an arsenal of horrific, readily transportable, and easily hidden weapons, including conventional explosives, nuclear weapons, and chemical and biological agents.

An Emerging Threat

Biowarfare and bioterrorism are emerging as particularly worrisome and insidious threats.[2] The Clinton administration National Security Strategy (NSS) included several references to the containment of the spread of biological weapons and enhancement of domestic preparedness for a biological weapons attack.[3] President Clinton became personally engaged in the issue, reportedly after reading *The Cobra Event*, Richard Preston's 1997 novel about a bioterrorism attack on New York City.[4] Yet, despite this high-level concern and attention, the Nation remains poorly prepared to deal with a biological attack. Of particular concern, there is not yet a cohesive national strategy to address a bioterrorism threat.[5] Current policies are inadequate to address terrorism attacks because there are no provisions for attribution or retribution.[6]

Defining Bioterrorism and Biological Agents

Terminology relating to bioterrorism can be confusing. The Federal Bureau of Investigation (FBI) defines *terrorism* as a "deliberate act or threat committed by an individual or group for political or social objectives."[7] This definition evidently does not preclude terrorism carried out by sovereign nations. With greater specificity, the U.S. General Accounting Office (GAO) defines *terrorist* as a "a non-state actor not provided with a state-developed weapon."[8] Complicating the issue, Rebecca Hersman and Seth Carus note the increasing difficulty of distinguishing between not only a terrorist event and an act of war but also terrorist and military use of chemical and biological weapons (CBW).[9] For example, they suggest that state adversaries may use terrorist surrogates to carry out attacks on civilian or military targets. Furthermore, biological attacks carried out by individuals or small groups for nonwarfare or nonpolitical purposes (especially for economic objectives) may be more properly described as *biocrimes*. [10] This paper simplifies the terminology by considering terrorism as a hostile, covert act committed by any inimical interest against an individual, interest, or group for political, economic, or social gain that occurs outside the framework of a formally declared war.

Although terrorists may employ a wide variety of means to accomplish objectives, from acts of vandalism and violence to the use of conventional or unconventional weapons, most observers are concerned about the potential employment of weapons of mass destruction (WMD) by terrorists. The General Accounting Office defines *WMD* as "chemical, biological, and nuclear weapons or agents."[11] Others have added *radiological* to this listing and use the acronym *CBRN* (chemical, biological, radiological, and nuclear) to describe devices of mass destruction.[12]

Carus defines *bioterrorism* as "the threat or use of biological agents by individuals or groups motivated by political, religious, ecological, or other ideological objectives."[13] Paul Rogers, Simon Whitby, and Malcolm Dando cite a Federal Government definition of *biological warfare* as "the intentional cultivation or production of pathogenic bacteria, fungi, viruses . . . and their toxic products, as well as certain chemical compounds, for the purpose of producing disease or death."[14] In this paper, biological warfare (synonymous with *biowarfare*) denotes the hostile use of biological agents against an enemy in the context of a formally declared war. Bioterrorism is considered an act of terrorism that employs biological agents. Although this paper focuses on bio*terrorism* (considered synonymous with *biological terrorism*), much of the discussion also applies to biological *warfare* or *biocrimes*—the consequences of which are likely to be similar whether conducted by a nation-state during a formally declared war or by a hostile actor outside of war.

Biological agents that could be employed as biological weapons include living organisms (micro-organisms and macro-organisms), chemical products of living organisms (including biological toxins), manufactured substances that mimic the action of biological substances,[15] and genetically modified organisms.[16] Some 39 agents have been identified as potential bioweapons.[17] Among biological agents, anthrax and smallpox have the greatest potential for mass human casualties and disruption.[18] Both agents are highly lethal; stable enough to be applied as an aerosol; capable of large-scale production; and have already been weaponized by hostile nations (anthrax by Iraq and both anthrax and smallpox by Russia). There are limited vaccines for both agents, and there would likely be a delay before their effects are recognized. Each would carry a powerful psychological punch as well. Other agents of significant human concern include plague, tularemia, botulinum toxins, and viral hemorrhagic fevers, such as Ebola.[19]

Scientists have recently expressed concern that terrorists could exploit the potential for the creation of life forms using new knowledge about the gene sequences of living organisms. This technology could result in the manufacture of genetically engineered pathogens, toxins, or synthetic *superbugs*, which could be employed as biological weapons or even programmed to target specific ethnic groups.[20] Russian scientists recently reported that they have developed a genetically engineered anthrax strain that is resistant to the vaccine currently being given to U.S. troops.[21]

Terrorists could also develop and deploy a cocktail involving multiple biological agents or a combination of biological and chemical agents, severely impeding efforts to identify the cause of illness and to provide effective treatment. Saddam Hussein employed a chemical cocktail involving multiple agents in his attack on the predominantly Kurdish Iraqi town of Halajba in March 1988.[22] Soviet émigré Kenneth Alibek, former first deputy chief of *Biopreparat*—the biological weapons program of the former Soviet Union—is concerned that Russian scientists may have recently developed a recombinant virus containing genetic components of both Ebola and smallpox virus.[23]

The most effective biological weapon agents would be highly infectious, communicable, and lethal; efficiently dispersible; easily produced in large quantities; stable in storage; resistant to environmental degradation; and lacking vaccines or effective treatments.[24] Biological agents may be targeted directly against humans through injection or topical application; deployed against agricultural crops, livestock, poultry, and fish; applied as a contaminant of food or drinking water; disseminated as an aerosol; or introduced through a natural vector such as an insect.[25] Motives of terrorists may include commission of selective or mass murder; incapacitation of enemies; achievement of political goals; undermining of social stability or creation of mass panic; or pursuit of economic objectives through destabilization, blackmail, extortion, or market disruptions.[26] Potential perpetrators cover the spectrum from hostile nation-states and large, well-funded, and possibly state-supported organizations to small, political or religious extremist groups such as the Aum Shinrikyo, the Japanese sect responsible for the sarin gas attack in a Tokyo subway system in 1995.[27] Even disaffected individuals could be bioterrorists.

Biological warfare (BW) agents are easily distinguished from chemical warfare (CW) agents. Unlike BW agents, CW agents do not involve the use of living organisms for their application or manufacture. In addition, CW agents are targeted against specific areas to achieve tactical effects. In contrast, BW agents can have enduring effects over very large areas to achieve strategic objectives.

Biological Agents as Weapons: Pros and Cons

Biological agents have much to make them appropriate as weapons of warfare or terrorism—whether employed against humans or used to attack agricultural targets (see table 1). First, they are relatively easy and inexpensive to obtain from culture collections or to produce.[28] Saddam Hussein purchased his base anthrax culture from an American mail order biological supply company, which obliged the dictator by shipping it via overnight express.[29] Kathleen Bailey, formerly with the U.S. Arms Control and Disarmament Agency, reportedly believes that a substantial biological weapons arsenal could be constructed in a 15-by-15-foot room at a cost of $10,000—the price of a beer fermenter, a protein-based culture, a gas mask, and a plastic lab coat.[30] Compounding the problem of ease of manufacturing biological agents is that the technology to produce them is dual-use, which means that they could also be put to such benign and legitimate purposes as fermentation or vaccine manufacturing. These purposes could easily provide cover to the would-be terrorist.[31] This presents significant challenges to implementing an effective verification program for any international protocol or convention banning biological weapons.[32]

Silent, invisible, microscopic, and odorless, biological agents can be introduced without fanfare and strike without warning. Because

Table 1. Selected antipersonnel biological agents

Agent	Type	Effect on humans	Notes
Pathogens			
Anthrax (*Bacillus anthracis*)	Bacteria	95–100 percent mortality in untreated persons	Entry inhalatory or cutaneous; only cutaneous form is contagious; spores stable and persistent
Ebola (*Filoviriodae*)	Virus	50–90 percent mortality	Highly contagious and infectious via aerosols
Plague (*Yersinia pestis*)	Bacteria	100 percent mortality in untreated persons	Disease carried by fleas; also known as Bubonic plague and Black Death. Can be delivered in aerosol form
Q-fever (*Coxiella burnetii*)	Rickettsia	Mortality less than 1 percent	Rarely contagious
Smallpox (*Ortho pox-virus variolua*)	Virus	High mortality	Highly contagious. Disease eradicated in 1980 but stocks remain in the United States, Russia, and maybe elsewhere
Tularemia (*Francisella tularensis*)	Bacteria	30–40 percent mortality	Infectious at low doses in untreated persons
Toxins			
Botulinum toxin or botulism (*Clostridium botulinum*)	Bacterial toxin	60–90 percent mortality	Noncontagious in untreated persons
Ricin	Toxin from castor bean	—	Historical assassination agent

Sources: Lois R. Ember, "Bioterrorism: Countering the Threat," *Chemical and Engineering News* 77, no. 27 (July 5, 1999); and Mark G. Kortepeter and Gerald W. Parker, "Potential Biological Weapons Threat," *Emerging Infectious Diseases* 5, no. 4 (July/August 1999), available at <http://www.cdc.gov/ncidod/EID/vol5no4/kortepeter.htm>.

micro-organisms readily reproduce in hosts at rapid rates, a tiny amount of pathogen, properly introduced, can quickly cause a devastating infection. An infection in the host can then be transmitted rapidly to nearby members of the population. An infection may go undetected or undiagnosed for days; thus, a major disease outbreak could be well under way before medical, veterinary, or agricultural authorities are alerted.

Another advantage of biowarfare, or bioterrorism, is the wide range of effects that biological agents can confer on victims, ranging from near-certain mortality to temporary disability. The toxins of some living organisms—including microscopic bacteria, viruses, and venomous snakes and marine animals—are among the most poisonous agents known. In fact, some biological agents are more lethal than thermonuclear weapons; by one calculation, 100 kilograms of anthrax, effectively dispersed, could kill twice as many people as a one-megaton nuclear warhead.[33] Other biological agents may cause short-term incapacitation. Consequently, biological agents can be selected and employed according to the specific military, political, or economic objective. Mortality is not necessarily required to accomplish the objective. Furthermore, authorities may be persuaded that a disease outbreak is natural, providing cover or plausible deniability to biological terrorists.[34] This is exemplified by the outbreak of West Nile virus in the greater New York area in the summer of 1999. Authorities have been unable to determine if the exotic disease, never before identified in America, was a naturally transmitted infection or an act of bioterrorism.[35] The investigation has been complicated by a report, prior to the outbreak, that Iraq was developing and planning to deploy a strain of the virus as a bioweapon.

Use of biological agents as weapons offers significant psychological advantages to terrorists, triggering primal fear reactions among humans familiar with the horrors of Dark Age plagues and popularized accounts of hypothetical or real modern-day disease outbreaks, such as Mad Cow disease and Ebola virus.[36] Even the threat of bioterrorism could cause panic in populations, providing substantial leverage to terrorists. Bioterrorism may also exploit fundamental national vulnerabilities—including porous borders, an open society, and dense population centers—and severely challenge the public health infrastructure, which presently does not have the experience, surveillance capability, or treatment capacity to monitor or respond to massive, widespread, and simultaneous disease outbreaks.[37] Finally, it is important to recognize that during the Cold War, the approach of the U.S. national security community was to describe a threat first (by collecting incriminating intelligence) and then to formulate an appropriate response. In the post-Cold War era of asymmetric threats, a clear understanding of national vulnerabilities is a prerequisite to identifying and elucidating a threat.[38]

While biological agents have many benefits as instruments of warfare or terror, they are not ideal weapons, particularly in a battlefield situation. To be effective, most agents must be widely disseminated, infecting numerous targets simultaneously. The most effective dispersal method would be an aerosol cloud; however, microscopic pathogenic agents lose virulence or die rapidly on release because of exposure to ultraviolet radiation and desiccation. There are also substantial practical difficulties in controlling the dispersal path of the agents in unpredictable conditions of atmospheric or other transport.[39] Further, biological weapons, in contrast to high explosives, lack the overwhelming and immediate show of physical force that demoralizes enemies.[40]

Additional disadvantages of biological weapons include the need to protect handlers from accidental contamination; the difficulty of maintaining quality control and containment during manufacture and harvesting of agents; the poor survival in storage of agents; and the difficulty of maintaining biological weapons in a delivery state.[41] Finally, using water or food as a vector for biological contaminants or pathogens is complicated by the fact that agents would be diluted in water; potable water is routinely purified in municipal treatment facilities, and cooking food would destroy most (but probably not all) biological toxins or pathogens.[42]

Current and Future Threats

National and international authorities are beginning to sound the alarm that American agriculture is an increasingly likely target of biological warfare.[43] The concerns largely derive from expanding knowledge about bioweapons programs in other nations, including those inimical to the United States. As summarized in table 2, it is well documented that at least 17 nations have current known or suspected bioweapons programs and that another 12 nations conducted biowarfare programs in the past. It has also been well established that both Iraq and the former Soviet Union have had substantial anti-agriculture programs targeting the United States.

In contrast, there is considerable debate about the extent to which America in general, and the food and agriculture infrastructure in particular, are threatened by biological attacks carried out by terrorist organizations (as opposed to attacks by nation-states or criminal acts conducted by individuals). There are only two documented examples of biological attacks attempted by terrorist organizations (table 2). The first example is widespread food poisoning carried out by the Baghwan Shree Rajneesh cult in Oregon in 1984. The other example is a number of unsuccessful attempts by the Japanese-based Aum Shinrikyo organization,

Table 2. Nations and organizations with known or suspected current or historical capability or interest in biowarfare or bioterrorism

Nations with current known or suspected bioweapons programs	Status of program
Bulgaria	Suspected
China	Suspected
Cuba	Suspected
Egypt	Suspected
India	Suspected
Iran	Known
Iraq	Known, including anti-agriculture
Israel	Suspected
Libya	Known
North Korea	Known (30 years)
Pakistan	Suspected
Romania	Suspected
Russia	Suspected
South Africa	Suspected
Sudan	Suspected (links to Osama bin Laden)
Syria	Known
Taiwan	Suspected

Political/religious extremist groups implicated in bioterrorism	Incidents
Aum Shinrikyo (cult group)	Ten unsuccessful attempts to spread anthrax and botulinum toxin in Japan (1990–1995)
Bhagwan Shree Rajneesh (cult group)	Widespread food poisoning with *Salmonella* in 1984 (Oregon); 751 victims (no deaths); political goals
German Red Army Faction	Discovery of biological weapons and documents in France by police (1980)

in the early 1990s, to spread anthrax and botulinum toxin. The General Accounting Office considers bioterrorism to be an emerging threat but has concluded that terrorists are less likely to use biological weapons than conventional explosives.[44] It does consider the possibility that terrorist use of bioweapons may increase over the next decade and does acknowledge that there are substantial differences of opinion among experts regarding

Table 2. Nations and organizations with known or suspected current or historical capability or interest in biowarfare or bioterrorism
(continued)

Other extremist organizations that could employ bioterrorism include religious fundamentalist groups, animal rights extremists, ecoterrorists, politically motivated terrorists, criminal organizations, and drug cartels. It was recently reported that elements in Egypt loyal to Osama bin Laden obtained biological agents through the mail. Potential sources include former Warsaw Pact countries and some East Asian nations.

Nations with past biowarfare programs	History
Belgium	Biowarfare research program after World War I
Canada	Biowarfare research program after World War I. Program combined with the United States and Great Britain
France	Biowarfare research program after World War I
Germany	Ambitious biowarfare program including anti-livestock in World War I. Biowarfare research program in World War II
Great Britain	Biowarfare research program initiated after World War I. Program combined with Canada and U.S. agricultural biowarfare research program in World War II, with German beef industry potential target
Italy	Biowarfare research program after World War I
Japan	Biological warfare program from 1918 to 1945; included experiments on Chinese prisoners in Manchuria (1932–1945)
Netherlands	Biowarfare research program after World War I
Poland	Biowarfare research program after World War I
South Africa	Suspected extensive biowarfare program during apartheid years, directed against Rhodesian guerrillas; allegedly included agricultural biowarfare (for example, distribution of anthrax spores among cattle)
United States	Biowarfare research program initiated after World War I. Program combined with Canada and Great Britain. Offensive biowarfare program initiated in 1942. Program included research and development and large-scale production of weapons, including agricultural biowarfare agents. Program terminated by Presidential Executive Order in 1970
USSR/Russia	Biowarfare research program after World War I. Extensive program *(Biopreparat)* until early 1990s; included assassinations, accidental contamination of civilian populations, and development of agricultural biowarfare agents. Concerns persist that program was never terminated

the extent of the bioterrorism threat. GAO recommends the undertaking of sound threat and risk assessments to ensure that counterterrorism investments are wisely spent and that effective, well-coordinated preparedness programs are formulated and implemented.

Regardless of whether a biological attack, targeting food or agriculture, is carried out by hostile states, terrorists, or criminals, the consequences of such an attack could be devastating. Risks, however small, are ignored at peril. It may also be assumed that any entity that has the demonstrated interest or capability to conduct biological warfare could inflict biological agents on food and agriculture interests as well as on human populations.

Chapter Two

An Emerging Threat to Food Security

Agriculture is a critical national infrastructure. Agriculture's overall contribution to the Nation's gross domestic product (GDP) is over a trillion dollars a year—one-sixth of the national total GDP.[45] The food and agriculture sector is the Nation's largest employer. Although farming directly employs less than 3 percent of the U.S. population, one out of eight Americans works in an occupation directly supported by food production.[46]

With a solid research foundation and extensive infrastructure, the American farming system is the most productive and efficient in the world. As a consequence, Americans spend less than 11 percent of their disposable income on food, compared with a global average of 20 to 30 percent.[47] In 1998, the United States produced 48.1 percent of the world's soybeans, 41.5 percent of its corn, 20.5 percent of its cotton, 11.8 percent of its wheat, and over 16 percent of its meat.[48] Also, agriculture may have a critical regional impact; for example, in some Northern Plains states, farming accounts for over 10 percent of total employment and gross state product.[49]

Agricultural exports total over $50 billion annually, making the farm sector the largest positive contributor to the U.S trade balance.[50] Exports of American agricultural products account for 15 percent of all global agriculture exports.[51] The economic multiplier of a farm commodity is a measure of total economic activity associated with a commodity and is a reflection of the farm gate value for that commodity, plus the value accruing from transportation, marketing, and processing of the commodity.[52] The Department of Commerce has concluded that the economic multiplier of exported farm commodities is 20 to 1; this compares with a multiplier of less than 2 to 1 for domestic crop sales (and the manufacture of major weapon systems) and less than 3 to 1 for domestic livestock sales.

Potential Targets

There are five potential targets of agricultural bioterrorism: field crops; farm animals; food items in the processing or distribution chain; market-ready foods at the wholesale or retail level; and agricultural facilities, including processing plants, storage facilities, wholesale and retail food outlets, elements of the transportation infrastructure, and research laboratories. To date, concern about agricultural bioterrorism has focused primarily on field crops and farm animals on the production side. It is important to remember that bioterrorism attacks could also be directed against foods destined for near-term human consumption, or against facilities, including research laboratories engaged in investigations that may be offensive to extremist organizations.

Vulnerability of U.S. Agriculture

Despite the importance of agriculture to the U.S. economy and the well-being of American citizens, scant attention has been given to agricultural vulnerability to terrorist attack. Simply put, America is exceedingly vulnerable to agricultural bioterrorism. The reasons for this situation are numerous. To begin, there is limited appreciation for the economic and social importance of agriculture in the industrialized West. Abundant, affordable, and safe food supplies are largely taken for granted, and agricultural products are not viewed as vulnerable to significant disruption.[54] It is hard for American citizens to imagine a world where the availability of food radically changes for the worse.

Moreover, because of its large size and complexity, the U.S. agribusiness infrastructure is a tempting target,[55] and access to American farms and agribusiness facilities is comparatively easy.[56] Much of the agricultural industry is highly concentrated in monoculture (single species) croplands, livestock feedlots, poultry houses, and major food processing and distribution centers, making it relatively easy for infection or contamination to spread rapidly.[57] The extent of production concentration in agriculture is indicated by the fact that a large proportion of sales of individual commodities originates in a relatively small percentage of farms. For example, less than 10 percent of cow and calf production facilities, approximately 20 percent of American grain and vegetable and citrus farms, 25 percent of dairy cattle and pig farms, 33 percent of poultry farms, and about 45 percent of cotton farms account for 75 percent of U.S. sales of those commodities.[58]

The industry's widespread vertical integration (where a single company controls much of the commodity production, processing, and distribution system) also facilitates the geographical spread of pathogens.[59] This problem is exacerbated by the fact that the American retail food industry presently does not have established procedures for preventing food contamination by terrorists; therefore, it is highly vulnerable to such incidents because of the large number of undocumented workers in the industry, particularly in fast food restaurants.[60] Monitoring for deliberate terrorist contamination of foods in retail establishments is significantly complicated by the large number of potential food-borne pathogens that could be employed; by the current absence of continuous, in-line monitoring of food products; and by the difficulty of holding food items long enough at any point in the distribution process to enable precise and accurate detection of pathogens.[61] In addition, it would be difficult to distinguish between natural contamination by food-borne pathogens and a terrorist incident.

Current animal husbandry methods in the United States (including crowding, hormone injections, branding, dehorning, castration, and disinfectant sterilization) have increased stress levels in livestock and poultry, lowering their resistance to infection.[62] Also, limited genetic diversity in most U.S. agriculture species may make those species particularly vulnerable to specific pathogens.[63] Because American livestock and poultry are the most protected and healthiest in the world, vaccines are not routinely used. Moreover, because many foreign diseases are not endemic to the United States, animal agriculture is highly vulnerable to a non-endemic pathogen.[64] Widespread use of antibiotics to treat common diseases makes American animals vulnerable to antibiotic-resistant pathogen strains.[65]

Rapid advances in genetic engineering of commercial plants to confer enhanced performance or desirable traits have raised the prospect of the creation of transgenic plant pathogens, pests, or weeds that are resistant to conventional control methods.[66] This prospect has already been realized through the development of a genetically mutant *superweed*, which is reportedly resistant to current herbicides. The superweed was reportedly designed to "attack corporate monoculture" and target genetically engineered crops.[67] Pathogens developed for plant bioterrorism do not have to be highly specific for the targeted crop, thus making them easier to produce than human pathogens.[68] It could be hard to distinguish a bioterrorist attack from a natural outbreak of animal or plant disease, thus providing cover for a terrorist.[69] In contrast to humans and animals, signs of infection in plants may take some time to develop, delaying effective response by authorities.[70]

Compared with attacks against humans, attacks against agriculture are less risky to perpetrators. Anti-agriculture pathogens are generally safer to work with than human pathogens.[71] It also is easier to develop and deploy biological agents against agriculture than against humans: less technical knowledge is required.[72] In addition, public reaction may be less intense because, unless the goal is contamination of processed, ready-to-eat food, humans are not being directly targeted.[73] However, some livestock and poultry diseases are zoonotic, presenting the possibility that they could jump to humans, resulting in widespread human disease.

Although the economic consequences of a biological attack on U.S. agriculture are likely to be severe, penalties for agricultural biowarfare and bioterrorism prescribed by existing U.S. Code are trivial, and the record of prosecution has been sparse.[74] Financial losses would accrue from a number of interrelated consequences, including:[75]

- direct losses of agriculture commodities to diseases
- costs of diagnosis and surveillance
- required destruction of contaminated crops and animals to contain disease
- costs of disposal of mortalities and carcasses
- damage to consumer and public confidence
- need for long-term quarantine of infected areas
- losses due to export and trade restrictions
- disruption of commodity markets.

In fact, because the economic impact of terrorism directed against U.S. agriculture is likely to be substantial, the term *econoterrorism* has been proposed as an alternative to agricultural bioterrorism.[76]

When one considers the economic and social consequences of the natural outbreak of Mad Cow disease in England in the 1990s, the potential impacts of a well-coordinated, targeted bioterrorist act come into perspective. Mad Cow disease has already cost England between $9 billion and $14 billion in compensation costs to farmers and laid-off employees, and at least another $2.4 billion in loss of export markets.[77] These costs continue to escalate as confidence in British beef has been severely undermined; it will be exceedingly difficult to restore public confidence.

Consider another example. A devastating outbreak of Foot and mouth disease (FMD), a highly contagious viral disease of cloven-hoofed animals, was first reported in Taiwan in March 1997. FMD, comprising over 70 different strains, is the most infectious virus known, capable of spreading as a wind-driven aerosol over 170 miles from its source.[78] Within 6 weeks, FMD had spread throughout Taiwan, necessitating the slaughter of more than 8 million pigs and shutting down the nation's valuable pork exports.[79] The origin of the disease was reportedly traced to a single pig from Hong Kong, and China was suspected of deliberately introducing the disease into Taiwan.[80] The disease is still affecting Taiwan, and the ultimate costs to that nation are estimated to be at least $19 billion—$4 billion to diagnose and eradicate the disease and another $15 billion in indirect losses from trade embargoes.[81] Was this an act of biowarfare or bioterrorism? The answer may never be known, but it is a plausible hypothesis that it indeed was. The recent (spring 2001) outbreak of FMD in England could ultimately have even more devastating consequences than the Taiwan epidemic.

Could an FMD outbreak in America have similar consequences? Given the fact that the Nation's 100 million cattle, 70 million pigs, 10 million sheep, and over 40 million wild, cloven-hoofed animals are susceptible to the 70-odd strains of FMD in the world, America is at great risk for a devastating outbreak that could persist for years.[82] It has been estimated that even a limited outbreak affecting no more than 10 farms could have a $2 billion economic impact. Because one infected pig could release enough virus every day to infect, in theory, 100 million cows, it would be exceedingly difficult to contain the disease to such a small number of farms.[83]

FMD is by no means the only disease of livestock that would have devastating consequences if an outbreak occurred. A study published in 1994 projected the economic impact on the U.S. swine industry of an outbreak of African swine fever.[84] The authors concluded that the cost, over a 10-year period, would approximate $5.4 billion, a figure that could be three to five times higher today.

While the economic impact of bioterrorism against farm animals would be substantial, experts have concluded that an attack against American crops would have even greater consequences.[85] Crops comprise a larger percentage (54 percent) of the $202.3 billion farm gate value of American commodities than farm animals and their products and contribute more to exports.[86] More important, crops comprise the major components of prepared feeds for livestock, poultry, and farm-raised fish. Finally, deliberate contamination of processed foods by terrorists could have devastating consequences, not only in terms of human health, but also because of economic impact and loss of consumer confidence in the safety of the Nation's food supplies.

Agricultural Bioterrorism Agents

Just as there are a number of micro- and macro-organisms that could be employed in biological warfare against humans, a host of diverse bioweapons could be used against agriculture. These include microscopic pathogens, insects, weeds, and other organisms or biological substances. [87] Table 3 provides a summary of categories of biological agents that could be employed against agriculture.

There have been recent efforts to assess the anti-agriculture bioweapons potential and threat from the host of biological agents that could be used. Table 4 presents a comprehensive, unclassified listing developed for the Defense Intelligence Agency (DIA). Table 5 lists additional animal pathogens, not included in the DIA assessment, which other observers have identified. Both lists signify agents that cause animal diseases recognized as *List A* diseases by the Organization Internationale des Epizooties (OIE). List A diseases are considered not only to be highly infectious and capable of being widely and rapidly spread across international borders but also to have the potential to inflict catastrophic economic losses and social disruption. [88] List A diseases are rigorously monitored worldwide by OIE, whose member countries are required to report outbreaks of List A diseases within 24 hours of laboratory confirmation. Reports of List A outbreaks trigger immediate, severe trade restrictions on affected products. It is noteworthy that a number of existing or potential bioweapons pathogens are not included among the disease agents in List A (tables 4 and 5).

Historical Perspective

Biological warfare is not a recent phenomenon; in fact, there are many examples throughout history of lethal or debilitating biological agents being used against enemies. [89] Two millennia ago, the Romans dumped bodies into wells to foul enemy drinking water supplies. In the 14th-century siege of Kaffa, Tartars catapulted plague-infested bodies into the walled city to spread disease, perhaps triggering a subsequent outbreak of Bubonic plague that swept medieval Europe, causing 25 million deaths. Historians believe that an epidemic of smallpox that decimated Indian populations during the French and Indian War was attributable to

Table 3. Potential agricultural biowarfare or bioterrorism agents

Category/Agent	Potential target	Examples
Micro-organisms		
Bacteria, rickettsia	Commercial animals, plants, fish, food-borne pathogens	*Bacillus anthracis* (anthrax); *Xanthomonas* spp., botulinum toxin; *Salmonella* spp.
Viruses	Commercial animals, plants, fish, food-borne viruses	Foot and mouth disease; Avian influenza virus; African swine fever virus; Newcastle disease virus; banana bunch top virus
Fungi	Commercial plants, fish	South American wheat blight; corn seed blight; wheat smut; soybean rust; rice blast
Protozoans	Commercial animals, fish, food-borne protozoans	MSX disease of oysters; Whirling disease of fish; protozoan parasites
Microalgae	Commercial fish, shellfish	"Red Tide"; *Pfiesteria piscicida*
Macro-organisms		
Insects, worms	Commercial plants, animals	Boll weevil; screw worm; whitefly; wheat aphid; grape louse; Asian longhorn beetles; nematodes
Weeds	Commercial plants	—
Aquatic vertebrates and invertebrates	Commercial fish and shellfish	Lamprey eel; zebra mussel; sea lice
Biologically derived active substances	Commercial animals, plants, fish	—
Artificially designed biological-mimicking substances	Commercial animals, plants, fish	Biological toxins
Genetically modified organisms	Commercial animals, plants, fish	Superweeds and superbugs

Sources: "Bioterrorism May Be Threat to Crops," *USA Today* 128, no. 2655 (1999), 7; "Genetics Activists Create Superweed Kit," Cultural Terrorist Agency, January 24, 1999; Ronald E. Hurlbert, "Microbiology 101 Internet Text: Chapter XV, Addendum: Biological Weapons; Malignant Biology," 1999, accessed at <http://www.wsu.edu/~hurl bert/pages/101biologicalweapons.html>; Ronald P. Kadlec, "Twenty-First Century Germ Warfare," *Battlefield of the Future*, eds. Barry R. Schneider and Lawrence E. Grinter, Maxwell AFB, AL: Air University Press, 1995; Ronald P. Kadlec, "Biological Weapons for Waging Economic Warfare," eds. Schneider and Grinter; Norm W. Schaad et al., "Crop Biosecurity," APSnet, Abstracts of the 1999 American Phytopathological Society Annual Meeting Symposium: Plant Pathology's Role in Anti-Crop Bioterrorism and Food Security (September 15–October 31, 1999), available at <http://www.apsnet.org/online/feature/BioSecurity/Top.html>.

Table 4. Animal and plant pathogens with potential bioweapons application

Pathogens weaponized or pursued for weaponization potential	Additional pathogens with weaponization potential
Animal Pathogens	
African swine fever*	African horse sickness*
Anthrax	Avian influenza*
Foot and mouth disease*	Bluetongue*
Hog cholera/classical swine fever*	Bovine spongiform encephalopathy*
Ornithosis/Psittacocis	Contagious bovine pleuropneumonia*
Rinderpest*	Lumpy skin disease*
Trypanosomiasis	Newcastle disease*
Poxvirus	Paratuberculosis/Johne's disease
	Peste des petits ruminants
	Pseudorabies virus
	Rift valley fever*
	Sheep and goat pox*
	Swine vesicular disease*
	Vesicular stomatitis*
Plant Pathogens	
Rice blast *(Magnaporthe grisea)*	*Wheat Pathogens*
Wheat stem rust *(Puccinia graminis)*	Wheat dwarf geminivirus
Wheat smut *(Fusarium graminearum)*	Barley yellow dwarf virus
	Pseudomonas fascovaginaei
	Clavibacter tritic
	Corn Pathogens
	Barley yellow dwarf virus
	Pseudomonas fascovaginaei
	Scleropthora rayssiae
	(Brown stripe mildew)
	Peronoschlerospora sacchari
	(Sugarcane downy mildew)
	P. philippinensis
	(Philippine downy mildew)
	P. maydis (Java downy mildew)
	Soybeans
	Phakospora sachyrhizi (soybean rust)
	Soybean dwarf virus
	Pyrenochaeta glycines (Red leaf blotch)
	Cotton
	Fusarium oxysporum f. sp. Vasinfectum
	(Australian)
	Xanthomonas campestris pv.
	Maloacearium (Africa); Geminivirus

Source: Norm Steele, "Econoterrorism: U.S. Agricultural Productivity, Concentration, and Vulnerability to Biological Weapons," Unclassified Defense Intelligence Assessment for DOD Futures Intelligence Program, January 14, 2000.
    * Office Internationale des Epizooties List A Disease.

Table 5. Additional animal pathogens with bioweapons potential

Pathogens

Venezuelan equine encephalomyelitis virus

Teschen disease virus (Porcine enterovirus 1)

Porcine Enterovirus Type 9

Lyssa viruses and rabies viruses

Porcine reproductive and respiratory syndrome virus

Heartwater *(Cowdria ruminantium)*

Screw worm myiasis

Source: Terrance M. Wilson et al., "A Review of Agroterrorism, Biological Crimes, and Biological Warfare Targeting Animal Agriculture," draft manuscript, 2000.

the deliberate issue of smallpox-exposed blankets by the English to Indians presumed loyal to the French.

Given its relative ease and low risk, surprisingly few national or international incidents of agricultural bioterrorism have occurred. Carus has undertaken a comprehensive inventory and assessment of bioterrorism and biocrimes in the 20th century.[90] He has documented 222 cases, categorizing the cases and number of reported cases:

- confirmed use of biological agents 24
- probable or possible use 28
- threatened use (probable or confirmed possession) 11
- threatened use (no confirmed possession) 121
- confirmed possession (no known attempts or threats to use) 5
- probable or possible possession 6
- possible interest in acquisition (no known possession) 13
- false cases and hoaxes 14

It is surprising that there have been only 222 bioterrorism-related incidents in a 100-year period and that in only 24 cases have there been confirmed attacks—an average of 1 every 4 years worldwide. Furthermore, only one attack resulted in mass human casualties—the *Salmonella* contamination of food by the Rajneeshee cult in Oregon in 1984.[91]

Fourteen of the 24 confirmed cases of bioterrorism or biocrimes are food or agriculture-related; of these cases, 11 involved food poisoning and only 3 targeted commercial animals or plants (table 6). Of the 222

Table 6. Selected agricultural or food bioterrorism incidents in the 20th century

Year	Nature of incident	Alleged perpetrators
Confirmed Use		
1997	Spreading rabbit hemorrhagic virus among wild rabbit population in New Zealand	New Zealand farmers
1996	Food poisoning in Texas hospital using Shigella	Hospital lab worker
1995	Food poisoning of estranged husband using ricin	Kansas physician
1984	Food poisoning of residents of The Dalles, Oregon, using *Salmonella* in restaurant food	Rajneesh religious cult
1970	Food poisoning of Canadian college students	Estranged roommate
1970	Food poisoning with typhoid and dysentery agents	Japanese physician
1952	Use of plant toxin to kill livestock	Mau Mau (Kenya, Africa)
1939	Food poisoning via *Salmonella*-contaminated pastry	Japanese physician
1936	Food poisoning via *Salmonella* (typhoid)	Japanese physician
1932	Attempted food poisoning of Lytton Commission members investigating Manchuria takeover via fruit contaminated with cholera	Japanese military
1916	Food poisoning involving numerous pathogens	New York dentist
1915	Infection of U.S. and allied draft animals and livestock with glanders and anthrax	German intelligence
1913	Food poisoning of family members with cholera and typhus organisms (Germany)	Former employee of chemist's shop
1912	Food poisoning using poisonous mushrooms	Frenchman trained as a druggist

Threatened use (not related to food poisoning)

Year	Description	Perpetrator
1989	Threat to release "Medflies" (fertile Mediterranean fruit flies) in California to infect crops in protest against pesticide spraying	The "Breeders," an extremist environmental group
1984	Attempt to kill a race horse with pathogens (insurance scam, confirmed possession)	Two Canadians
1984	Threat to spread Foot and mouth disease to wild pigs, which would then spread disease to livestock (no confirmed possession)	Australian prison inmate
1980	Threat to use biological agents against crops (no confirmed possession)	Tamil guerrillas, Sri Lanka
1970	Epidemic of African hog fever virus in Cuba alleged to have been deliberately inflicted by the United States (false case, no evidence)	U.S. Government (CIA)

Source: W. Seth Carus, "Bioterrorism and Biocrimes: The Illicit Use of Biological Agents in the 20ᵗʰ Century," Center for Counterproliferation Research, National Defense University (August 1998; July 1999 revision).

The following additional incidents are reported by other sources:

–1997: Foot and mouth disease outbreak in Taiwan necessitated slaughter of eight million pigs. China suspected of "agro-sabotage." See "U.S. Could Face New New Terror Tactic: Agricultural Warfare," *The Philadelphia Inquirer*, June 22, 1999; Grant Robertson, "Crop Warfare Combat Plan Urged," *Calgary Herald*, August 21, 1999.

–Mid 1990s: Poisoning of Nestle food products for extortion purposes by a German metal worker (nature of poison not related). Perpetrator was convicted. See "Man Who Poisoned Food Gets 11-Year Jail Term," *The Boston Globe*, September 24, 1999, A16.

–1985: Outbreak of screw worm parasite, which affects both animals and people, in Mexico. Believed to be deliberately caused by disgruntled workers at a U.S. screw worm eradication research laboratory in Mexico. See "Agriculture Fears Terrorist Threats to Food Supply," *Department of Energy and Nuclear Regulatory Commission Monthly Terrorism and Security Report* 3, no. 10 (October 1999); Judith Miller, "U.S. To Use Lab for More Study of Bioterrorism," *The New York Times*, October 8, 1998, 26.

–1982–1984: Infection of horses with glanders perpetrated by Russian military forces in Afghanistan. See Terrance M. Wilson et al., "A Review of Agroterrorism, Biological Crimes, and Biological Warfare Targeting Animal Agriculture," draft manuscript, 2000.

–1978–1980: Poisoning of cattle with anthrax by Rhodesian security forces in South Africa. Ibid.

documented incidents, only 6 appear to be clearly linked to attacks on commercial plants and animals (table 6).

One sobering statistic from the Carus survey is that 144 incidents occurred in the 1990s—nearly two-thirds of the total. This may reflect better incident tracking and record keeping in recent years, or it may indicate a dramatic increase in the propensity of terrorists or criminals to employ biological agents. Available evidence supports the latter premise. For example, FBI statistics indicate that U.S. incidents involving weapons of mass destruction using chemical, biological, radiological, or nuclear materials have soared from 37 in 1996 to over 200 in 1999, with three-fourths of the cases involving biological agents—usually the threatened release of anthrax.[92] Notably, the vast majority of incidents have been directed against individuals or small groups, not mass populations.

Terrorism by Animal Rights Extremists

One additional category of agriculture-related terrorism merits close attention: acts of violence or vandalism conducted by animal rights extremists.[93] Though often directed against the agricultural infrastructure, these acts are not technically considered agricultural bioterrorism because they do not typically involve the use of biological agents (although they could), and they may target commercial animal enterprises that are not strictly agricultural (for example, pet shops, zoos, aquariums, rodeos, and circuses). There is strong evidence that these incidents are increasing.

In response to the Animal Enterprise Protection Act of 1992, the Department of Justice (DOJ) and the Department of Agriculture jointly provided Congress with a comprehensive report on the extent and effects of domestic and international terrorism on animal enterprises through 1992. The Act defines *animal enterprise* as "1) a commercial or academic enterprise that uses animals for food or fiber production, agriculture, research, or testing; 2) a zoo, aquarium, circus, rodeo, or lawful competitive animal event; or 3) any fair or similar event intended to advance the agricultural arts and sciences."[94] The report identified 313 incidents of terrorism involving 28 different kinds of animal enterprises by animal rights extremists between 1977 and June 1993. Of these incidents, 79 targeted agriculture or food enterprises, including agricultural or food production facilities (28 incidents); markets, delis, or butcher shops (33); restaurants (6); breeding ranches (7); fur-animal farms or breeders (3); and feed cooperatives (2). In addition, 63 incidents occurred at university medical and research facilities, 21 at private research facilities, laboratories, or medical centers, 8 at Federal research or medical facilities, and 3 at local government facilities.

In a more recent report, the National Animal Interest Alliance cited 42 incidents of such terrorism conducted by animal rights extremists between 1996 and 1999, of which 35 occurred in the United States.[95] Incidents included the release of domesticated animals raised for the fur trade; attacks on animal research facilities, pet stores, restaurants, supermarkets, slaughterhouses and meatpacking plants; and threats against farmers.

Most incidents perpetrated by animal rights extremists have involved vandalism or theft and release of animals. There have been no documented attacks that involved the use of biological agents. Nonetheless, the potential for animal rights extremists or ecoterrorists to employ biological agents should be taken seriously.

Chapter Three

Countering the Threat

Current Federal Frameworks and Initiatives

Understanding government roles and responsibilities in preparing for and responding to acts of terrorism is complicated by the fact that a plethora of Federal, state, and local agencies and programs have important, often overlapping responsibilities for activities that are directly applicable to terrorism. To begin, there is in place a substantial framework—the Federal Response Plan (FRP)—for managing Presidentially declared disasters. The Disaster Relief Act of 1974 (as amended by the Stafford Act in 1988) defines *disaster* as "all conceivable manmade or natural occurrences whose catastrophic consequences could lead to a (state) governor's request for Federal assistance."[96] Presidential declarations of major disasters or emergencies have usually been invoked for weather-related events, but a recent annex to the FRP ("Terrorism Incident Annex") now includes terrorism in the FRP framework.

While the Federal Emergency Management Agency (FEMA) has overall responsibility for Federal disaster assistance, FRP recognizes that local governments have the primary responsibility for preparing for and managing disasters that affect communities. FRP sets forth policies, plans, and structures by which the Federal Government "mobilizes resources and conducts activities to augment state and local response and recovery efforts."[97] FRP also clarifies the roles of 27 Federal departments and agencies in providing disaster assistance. Key areas of responsibilities and primary responsible agencies include:

- transportation (Department of Transportation)
- communications (National Communications System)
- public works and engineering (U.S. Army Corps of Engineers and DOD)
- firefighting (Forest Service and USDA)

- information and planning (FEMA)
- mass care (American Red Cross)
- resource support (General Services Administration)
- health and medical services (Health and Human Services)
- urban search and rescue (FEMA)
- hazardous materials (Environmental Protection Agency)
- food (Food and Nutrition Service and USDA)
- energy (Department of Energy).

Catastrophic, highly publicized terrorist incidents (for example, the bombings of the World Trade Center in 1993, the Alfred P. Murrah Federal Building in Oklahoma City, and American Embassies in Africa, as well as the sarin nerve gas attack in Tokyo in 1995) have pushed the Federal Government to develop a separate but related framework for consequence management, with specific application to WMD incidents and terrorism. Presidential Decision Directive (PDD) 39, issued in June 1995, designated the FBI as the lead Federal agency for response to domestic terrorism incidents. In 1996, Congress passed the Anti-Terrorism and Effective Death Penalty Act (P.L. 104–132), which established national policy to counter terrorism involving weapons of mass destruction directed against personnel. In the same year, Congress passed the Defense Against Weapons of Mass Destruction Act of 1996 (P.L. 104–201, "Nunn-Lugar-Domenici Act"), which authorizes DOD to develop a Domestic Preparedness Program to combat terrorism.[98]

Building on PDD 39, President Clinton issued two new decision directives in 1998: PDD 62, "Combating Terrorism," and PDD 63, "Critical Infrastructure Protection." Establishing a new National Coordinator for Security, Critical Infrastructure, and Counter-Terrorism in the National Security Council to coordinate the policies in both directives has effectively linked these two PDDs.[99] The structure linking PDD 62 and 63 is envisioned to provide a coordinated mechanism to address critical infrastructure protection and terrorism through three interagency groups: WMD Preparedness Group; Counter-Terrorism Security Group; and Critical Infrastructure Protection Group. In addition to the NSC, 10 Federal departments (Defense, Justice, Energy, State, Agriculture, Health and Human Services, Commerce, Treasury, Interior, and Transportation) and 7 independent Federal agencies (Office of Management and Budget, Office of Science and Technology Policy, Nuclear Regulatory Commission, Environmental Protection Agency, Central Intelligence Agency, Federal Emergency Management Agency, and General Services Administration) were designated responsibilities for WMD and terrorism issues.[100] In addition, the

National Science Foundation supports major research programs that could support science-based counterterrorism initiatives. The Federal framework, under PDD 62 and 63, for national coordination for security, infrastructure protection, and counterterrorism is presented in appendix A.

Agriculture and Food Safety was identified as one of eight subgroups in the NSC structure, with USDA in a nominal coordinating role. In addition to the framework provided by PDD 62, a number of Federal programs to coordinate efforts to combat terrorism have been established in various agencies, including:

- National Domestic Preparedness Office and the Domestic Terrorism/Counterterrorism Planning Section (FBI)
- Office of Emergency Preparedness, National Disaster Medical System (Health and Human Services)
- Office of Emergency Response (Department of Energy)
- Defense Threat Reduction Agency (a new DOD agency reporting to the Under Secretary for Acquisition and Technology)
- Federal Emergency Management Agency, Federal Response Plan, Rapid Response Information System (RRIS)
- National Response Center and National Response Team (EPA).

Appendix C depicts Federal agencies and programs—more than 40 altogether—with responsibilities or capabilities for counterterrorism. Appendix D provides more detailed information on key Federal antiterrorism programs with specific applicability to bioterrorism and biowarfare.

Efforts to strengthen the Federal role in anti- or counterterrorism, including combating bioterrorism, have largely focused on DOD because of its specialized expertise in consequence management and unique capabilities to deter and respond to WMD attacks.[101] In turn, DOD has enhanced its ability to work closely with civilian authorities through the creation of a Joint Task Force for Civil Support under the newly established Joint Forces Command.[102] The Office of Management and Budget requested $10 billion for Federal programs to combat terrorism in the fiscal year 2000 budget.[103] Funding for fiscal year 1999 was $9.647 billion.[104]

Preparedness for Countering Terrorism

Despite these programs, initiatives, and capabilities, there is still widespread concern that the Nation is poorly prepared to combat terrorism in general and bioterrorism in particular.[105] Credible observers have expressed many concerns. For instance, there is no official definition of *consequence management*, nor an official explication of the relationship between consequence management and disaster preparedness or response.[106] The Department of State (responsible for consequence management abroad) has nine separate definitions for consequence management; DOD has two; and FEMA has its own separate definition. All of these definitions "differ on the scope and type of disasters that would be addressed by consequence management."[107] Similarly, terminology related to terrorism is confusing and often ambiguous.[108] For example, there are multiple definitions among different Federal agencies and others for *weapons of mass destruction, mass casualties,* and *terrorism.*

The large and growing number of Federal agencies involved in counterterrorism efforts complicates program management and coordination. There is existing and potential overlap among programs.[109] Also, Congressional roles and responsibilities for counterterrorism issues are dispersed among several committees.[110] There is no overarching strategy with a clear definition of *end state* to guide Federal efforts to manage potential WMD incidents.[111] Development of Federal budgets for counterterrorism has occurred in the absence of "soundly established, defined, and prioritized program requirements" that cut across agencies.[112]

No credible national-level risk assessment has been undertaken of potential chemical and biological terrorism.[113] This lack has resulted in disagreement among authorities regarding terrorist threats and preoccupation with worst-case scenarios.[114] Timely and accurate sharing of information about terrorist threats is impeded by national security considerations in regard to protecting classified intelligence data.[115] While combating terrorism is a national responsibility, domestic response to emergencies is almost always a state and local responsibility. In the case of terrorism incidents, apportionment of Federal responsibilities is complicated by the complex Federal structure relating to terrorism and weapons of mass destruction.[116]

More problematic, there has not yet been clear designation of overall Federal leadership for domestic counterterrorism. PDD 62 did establish a National Coordinator for Security, Critical Infrastructure, and Counter-Terrorism in the National Security Council. In addition, on October 8, 2001, Pennsylvania Governor Tom Ridge was sworn in as the director of a new White House Office of Homeland Security. By reporting directly to the President, the director has substantial authority to improve the focus and effectiveness of the complex Federal antiterrorism bureaucracy. However, even though a National Coordinator in the NSC and new Office of Homeland Security will bring greatly needed order to the Federal counterterrorism structure, coordination should not be confused with leadership. Complicating matters, a number of Federal agencies have been assigned various counterterrorism leadership roles. The National Domestic Preparedness Office in the FBI has been tasked with developing a national strategy to address domestic preparedness.[117] PDD 39 designates the FBI as the "lead Federal agency for crisis response in the event of a terrorist incident in the United States" and identifies FEMA as the "lead Federal agency for consequence management."[118] The boundary between a *crisis* and a *consequence management* situation is, at best, diffuse.[119] There is similar fragmented or uncertain leadership for responding to terrorist attacks on U.S. civilians or support infrastructures overseas.[120] DOD does have clear responsibility for responding to terrorist attacks on the Armed Forces and military facilities in foreign lands, but not for attacks on U.S. civilian personnel and facilities where a State Department lead is likely.

While DOD would assume primary leadership in the event of terrorist attacks on domestic military installations and personnel, probable collateral effects on civilian populations (particularly if bioweapons are employed) would necessitate shared responsibilities and close coordination with civilian agencies. Hersman and Carus point out that the DOD role in responding to terrorism is complicated by the increasingly blurred line between an act of warfare (where DOD would have lead responsibility) and an act of terrorism (where civilian agencies would have major responsibilities).[121] Complicating the situation still further, responsibilities for *preventing* or *deterring* terrorism are even less well defined than for *managing the consequences* of terrorism.

Countering Agricultural Bioterrorism

As inadequately prepared as America is to combat terrorism in general, the Nation is even less prepared to counter terrorism directed against the food and agriculture infrastructure. Agricultural bioterrorism has gotten little attention in Federal counterterrorism initiatives.[122] There are three principal reasons for this lack of attention. First, Americans take food for granted. With availability of abundant, safe, and affordable food the status quo for most of the 20th century, citizens find difficulty in conceiving of circumstances under which food would be scarce, expensive, or risky to consumers. Second, the national visibility of agriculture has been declining for decades. Though the United States produces more food than ever, far fewer Americans are involved in its production. Farming accounted for 2.6 percent of U.S. employment in 1998—down from 23 percent in 1929—and the number of American farms declined from 6.3 million to 2.2 million in the same period.[123] Finally, there is limited public or official awareness of the potential threat of bioterrorism directed against food and agriculture. Most Americans think immediately and exclusively of human diseases when considering bioterrorism.

Consequently, agriculture is not included among the eight critical national infrastructures identified in PDD 63, "Critical Infrastructure Protection."[124] Agriculture and Food Safety is identified as one of eight subgroups of the Weapons of Mass Destruction Preparedness group in the new NSC WMD and Terrorism structure established by PDD 62.[125] USDA serves as chair of this subgroup; however, this department is a relative newcomer to national security and defense structure and presently lacks requisite visibility and clout to champion greater Federal attention to countering agricultural bioterrorism.[126] Agriculture tends to be overshadowed by other terrorism issues—including cyberterrorism and nuclear, chemical, and biological terrorism against humans—that already have the attention of the national defense community.

Even the catastrophic events of last September have failed to galvanize national attention to the American agriculture infrastructure. For example, a recent analysis of national vulnerability to chemical and biological attacks cited 39 articles in the popular press published since the terrorist attacks. Only one article made specific reference to potential attacks on U.S. food supplies.[127]

As a result, Federal efforts to develop a strategy to counter agricultural terrorism are hindered by limited funding to date. Federal and national attention to bioterrorism has been primarily focused on potential attacks against people, resulting in substantial new resources directed to counter terrorist-initiated human disease outbreaks. For example, counterterrorism funding in the Department of Health and Human Services increased from $13.8 million in fiscal year (FY) 1997 to $160 million in FY 1999. The budget request for FY 2000 was $230 million. In contrast, the food and agriculture sector has been largely ignored so far. No funds were specifically appropriated for USDA for counterterrorism in FY 1999 or requested in FY 2000.[128] The Agricultural Research Service (ARS) requested $391 million for fiscal year 2001 to support research to combat agricultural terrorism.[129] However, ARS FY 2001 appropriations specifically designated for counterterrorism research were only $500,000.

The terrorist attacks of September 11 have resulted in one encouraging response from Congress in regard to protecting the Nation's food supplies. Senators John Edwards and Chuck Hagel recently drafted new legislation entitled "The Biological and Chemical Weapons Preparedness Act of 2001." Among bill provisions are proposed appropriations ($250 million for FY 2002 and "such sums as may be necessary through [FYs] 2003 through 2006") for the Department of Agriculture for protecting the American food supply from biological or chemical terrorism.

Need for a Coordinated National Strategy

The United States ignores the potential for agricultural bioterrorism at its peril. The relative ease of a catastrophic bioweapons attack against the American food and agriculture infrastructure, and the devastating economic and social consequences of such an act, demand that the Nation pursue an aggressive, focused, coordinated, and stand-alone national strategy to combat agricultural bioterrorism. The strategy should build on counterterrorism initiatives already underway; leverage existing Federal, state, and local programs and capabilities; and involve key customers, stakeholders, and partners. USDA should lead the development of this strategy.

USDA Leadership of a Stand-Alone Initiative

USDA should provide strong Federal leadership to develop and manage a coordinated, stand-alone interagency plan and program to combat agricultural bioterrorism. Stand-alone attention is desirable for two reasons. First, if subsumed into larger national counterterrorism programs, agricultural concerns may be buried in the enormously complex Federal counterterrorism bureaucracy and may be overshadowed by human health issues, cyberterrorism, and more conventional military threats. This concern is borne by the lack of dedicated appropriations to combat agricultural bioterrorism. Second, the U.S. food and agriculture community is clearly distinct from the medical and public health community and the traditional national defense establishment. However, stand-alone attention should not be construed as acting in a vacuum. A national program to counter agricultural bioterrorism should not only be linked to other national counterterrorism programs through the PDD 62 structure but also should involve strategic partnerships between USDA and other agencies and organizations with programs and capabilities that can contribute to the agriculture program.

While USDA chairmanship of the Agriculture and Food Safety subgroup under PDD 62 seemingly provides USDA with a mandate to exercise Federal leadership, this mandate would be strengthened by clear administration and Congressional designation of leadership, initially through a Presidential Executive Order, and, subsequently, through legislation.

Formal designation of leadership should be accompanied by a requirement for USDA to develop, within a reasonable time period, a comprehensive agricultural counterterrorism plan, involving Federal, state, and local government agencies, as well as the private sector.

There are likely to be objections to a USDA-led, stand-alone program to combat agricultural bioterrorism. Other Federal agencies may have territory concerns, especially where overlapping jurisdictions already occur (for example, food safety responsibilities in the Food and Drug Administration at the Department of Health and Human Services and in the USDA Food Safety and Inspection Service). Agencies may also perceive that new funding targeting agricultural terrorism may detract from other funding initiatives. Some agencies may believe that agriculture is adequately addressed in the existing NSC antiterrorism framework, obviating the need for a separate initiative. Still others may not be convinced of a threat against agriculture—or may believe that agriculture is not a critical national infrastructure, thus not a priority for antiterrorism programs.

Other objections may come from outside the Federal government. State and local agencies with responsibilities for farm programs or public safety may not support substantial Federal involvement in what could be viewed as a regional or local issue. Agribusiness interests may oppose a counterterrorism initiative because they are not convinced of the threat, because of the potential expense to taxpayers, or because of concerns that elevated public awareness may reduce confidence in the safety of the Nation's food and integrity of its agriculture systems.

These objections can be overcome. Skepticism about the threat can be addressed by a thorough, objective threat and risk assessment that provides a sound basis for an action plan and proposed budget. Concerns about territory and competing budgets can be offset by involving all relevant agencies in a counterterrorism plan; clarifying roles and responsibilities; ensuring that budget initiatives include appropriate funding for agencies with relevant programmatic responsibilities; building strategic partnerships; and ensuring effective, ongoing communications.

USDA should lead the development of an agricultural bioterrorism strategy because it has overall Federal responsibility for food safety and security; it has a broad range of programs to deter and respond to threats against food and agriculture (including natural disease outbreaks); and it is exceedingly well-connected to the national agribusiness spectrum through an extensive network of field offices, agricultural extension specialists, research facilities, and land-grant universities. In fact, USDA may be unique among Federal agencies in its closeness to constituencies. Randall Murch, formerly of the Advanced Systems and Concepts Office at the Defense Threat Reduction Agency, appreciates these points. Dr. Murch has a background in plant pathology and is aware of the unique expertise and experience required for protection of the Nation's food and agriculture infrastructure. He is supportive of USDA providing leadership for a coordinated, interagency program to combat agricultural bioterrorism, while recognizing the challenges presented by this role.[130] The consequences of a successful terrorist attack against agriculture could be devastating—in terms of both its economic impact and the undermining of public confidence in the Nation's food supply. Given the potential risks—and the fact that the United States is inadequately prepared to deter or respond to an attack—it cannot afford not to act.

Finally, an aggressive, well-coordinated effort to combat agricultural bioterrorism will have substantial ancillary benefits. Many antiterrorism actions could simultaneously help improve food safety for consumers and prevent or contain natural livestock and crop diseases, including an abundance of newly emerging diseases. Natural diseases cost U.S. agriculture billions of dollars annually. In addition, the effort will likely strengthen partnerships and improve coordination among agencies and organizations with responsibilities, programs, and capabilities to address a significant national threat. Because the threat is, arguably, more focused and manageable than other potential threats against the national infrastructures, an effective, coordinated program may provide a model for other counterterrorism efforts.

Relevant USDA Programs and Capabilities

USDA has substantial existing programs and capabilities that are directly applicable to combating agricultural bioterrorism. Key among these are programs in agricultural research and education, prevention and control of diseases and pests, and food safety.

Research and Education

The Agricultural Research Service (ARS) is the principal in-house research agency of USDA and is one of four agencies in the USDA Research, Education, and Economics (REE) mission area. ARS conducts research in over 100 national and international locations where approximately 1,900 ARS scientists carry out close to 1,100 research projects annually. The ARS appropriation was approximately $1 billion in FY 2001. It has proactively sought to strengthen agency capacity to conduct research to combat agricultural bioterrorism. ARS administers several major facilities that conduct research on animal diseases. The Plum Island Animal Disease Center (PIADC), located in New York state, undertakes "research and diagnosis to protect United States animal industries and exports against catastrophic economic losses caused by foreign animal disease (FAD) agents accidentally or deliberately introduced into the United States."[131] PIADC research is presently focusing on Foot and mouth disease and African swine fever. PIADC is collocated with the Foreign Animal Disease Diagnostic Laboratory (FADDL) of the Animal and Plant Health Inspection Service (APHIS) of USDA.

ARS also administers the National Animal Disease Center (NADC) in Ames, Iowa, the primary USDA facility for conducting research on animal diseases of economic importance to U.S. agriculture. NADC is located immediately adjacent to the APHIS National Veterinary Service Laboratories (NVSL) and the APHIS Center for Veterinary Biologics (CVB). The ARS Southeast Poultry Research Laboratory (SPRL) in Athens, Georgia, is the major USDA poultry health research facility for conducting research on exotic and emerging poultry diseases.

The Cooperative State Research, Education, and Extension Service (CSREES) is the USDA research agency that provides leadership for and works closely with the land-grant university system and other research and educational institutions in agricultural research and education endeavors, including extension education. CSREES partners with approximately 75 universities in all 50 states, the District of Columbia, and six U.S. territories. Appropriation is approximately $1 billion in FY 2001. As part of its education mission, CSREES supports the Extension Disaster Education Network (EDEN). EDEN is a collaborative, multistate network to provide agricultural extension educators and agents with ready access and linkages to information and resources related to disaster preparedness, recovery, and mitigation.[132]

The Economic Research Service (ERS) is the principal intramural economics and social science research agency of the department. ERS conducts research on the efficiency, equity, and efficacy of issues related to food safety and nutrition, rural development, and the environment. Appropriation in FY 2001 was approximately $66 million.

Prevention and Control of Diseases and Pests

The USDA Animal and Plant Health Inspection Service has the principal Federal responsibility for ensuring the health and care of animals and plants, including preventing and responding to outbreaks of diseases and pests affecting American agriculture. Two major divisions of APHIS—Veterinary Services and Plant Protection and Quarantine—carry out this responsibility, working closely with state and local veterinarians or plant or pest control officials. The Veterinary Services (VS) division of APHIS is responsible for protecting the farm animal industry, including livestock, poultry, and cultivated fish, from diseases. Personnel include veterinarians, scientists, epidemiologists, and diagnosticians. Since 1983, VS has administered a National Animal Health Monitoring System (NAHMS) to track the health and productivity of farm animals and establish a long-term database on American livestock and poultry diseases, disease conditions, and associated costs and production practices. NAHMS is coordinated through a Center for Animal Health Monitoring and conducted cooperatively with the farm animal industry.[133]

Veterinary Services also administers an Emergency Programs staff that works closely with private veterinarians to prepare for and respond to exotic animal disease outbreaks. Program components include surveillance systems to detect and diagnose diseases rapidly and coordinate prompt Federal and state responses through an animal health emergency plan.[134] VS administers its emergency response program through a formal organization, the Regional Emergency Animal Disease Eradication Organization (READEO). READEO works closely with state and local authorities to contain and respond to livestock disease outbreaks.[135]

Veterinary Services both employs a Field Epidemiologic Data System (FEDS), which is accessible to regional and national emergency management and response personnel,[136] and operates two major laboratories that serve as principal biocontainment reference centers for contagious and virulent animal diseases. One laboratory is in Ames, Iowa (National Veterinary Services Laboratories, immediately adjacent to the ARS National Animal Disease Center); the other is on Plum Island, New York (Foreign Animal Disease Diagnostic Laboratory, administered by ARS and co-located with the ARS Plum Island Animal Disease Center). Plum Island is the only U.S. location where studies can be conducted on foreign animal disease agents.[137]

The Plant Protection and Quarantine (PPQ) Division of APHIS is responsible for protecting American agricultural crops and plants from the national and international spread of diseases and pests.[138] Since 1982, PPQ has conducted a Cooperative Agricultural Pest Survey that gathers information about plant diseases, weeds, insects, and other pests and compiles it in a nationwide database called the National Agricultural Pest

Information System. If a foreign or exotic disease were discovered, PPQ would activate Rapid Response Teams to contain the disease. PPQ also administers the agricultural quarantine inspection (AQI) at airports, seaports, and borders. AQI is the Nation's first line of defense against the introduction of foreign diseases and pests.[139] APHIS also administers a Wildlife Services Division to manage agricultural problems, including diseases, caused by wildlife.

Food Safety

The Food Safety and Inspection Service (FSIS) is the USDA agency responsible for ensuring that the Nation's meat and poultry products are safe, wholesome, and correctly labeled and packaged. FSIS responsibilities are addressed in several pieces of legislation, including the Federal Meat Inspection Act and the Poultry Products Inspection Act. The service shares regulatory responsibilities for food safety with the Food and Drug Administration (FDA) of the Department of Health and Human Services. FDA is responsible for the safety of seafood, plant and dairy foods and beverages, and special nutritional products, including dietary supplements and infant formulas. FSIS also administers a number of programs to prevent or respond to outbreaks of food-borne illness.[140] These programs would constitute an effective framework for combating acts of deliberate food contamination by terrorists.

In 1996, FSIS implemented the Hazard Analysis and Critical Control Point (HACCP) regulatory system. This science-based system applies to slaughter and processing plants in the United States as well as in countries that export meat and poultry products to America. FSIS is expanding the HACCP program by undertaking a comprehensive farm-to-table approach to improve product safety at each step in the production, processing, distribution, and marketing process. FSIS is a partner in the Federal Food Safety Initiative launched in January 1997. The initiative includes improved food safety inspection and preventive measures; expanded research; development of a national early warning system for food-borne illness outbreaks; a national education campaign; and improved interagency coordination and program efficiency.

Since 1995, FSIS has been collaborating with the FDA, the Centers for Disease Control and Prevention, state health departments, and local investigators in a new program—the Food-borne Diseases Active Surveillance Network (FoodNet)—to track food-borne illness throughout America.[141] FoodNet initially targeted seven bacterial pathogens and established seven locations across the country to monitor incidents of food-borne illness and the effectiveness of food safety programs in preventing illness.[142] FSIS also administers the Animal Production Food Safety Program. This outreach and liaison program works with producers, researchers, and other relevant parties to apply scientifically based practices to the reduction of food safety risks during the raising of live food animals. FSIS is also involved with several programs to educate consumers about food safety. These programs include the dissemination of a variety of electronic and print-based information products; a USDA Meat and Poultry Hotline; the Fight BAC Campaign (a highly visible public education campaign similar to the "Smokey Bear" campaign); and participation in the Partnership for Food Safety Education, a coalition of Federal agencies, industry representatives, and consumer and public health organizations. If an incident of food contamination recalled a food product, the recall would be initiated by the Emergency Response Division (ERD) of FSIS, according to the category of risk presented by the contamination. Recalls are voluntary actions by food manufacturers or distributors, but ERD provides close oversight of recall actions.[143]

In addition to the programs described above, USDA and FSIS have undertaken several steps, in partnership with the FBI, Health and Human Services, and state and local health departments, to respond to acts or threats of deliberate contamination of food, including by terrorists.[144] FSIS has written procedures for investigating and responding to reports of deliberately or inadvertently contaminated food. A recall may be requested (but not mandated) if warranted by the investigation. USDA also has a Food Emergency Rapid Response and Evaluation Team, chaired by the Under Secretary of Food Safety, which brings together all departmental agencies (including FSIS) that could contribute to responding to a food emergency. This team is developing a response plan for deliberate acts or threats of contamination, including by terrorists. USDA and DOD jointly planned and conducted a multi-agency exercise, in August 1999, involving Federal response to a hypothetical terrorist act of deliberate biological contamination of FSIS-regulated food.

Other Relevant USDA Programs and Agencies

A number of additional USDA agencies have relevant responsibilities and capabilities that could contribute directly to a coordinated, department-wide effort to combat agricultural bioterrorism. The Farm Service Agency (FSA) administers farm commodity programs; farm ownership, operating, and emergency loans; conservation and environmental programs; emergency and disaster assistance; and domestic and international assistance and international export programs.[145] A particular strength of FSA is its grassroots organization: FSA delivers services to the farming community through an extensive network of field offices, including over 2,500 USDA Service Centers and 51 offices in every state and Puerto Rico. Elected committees, comprised of local farmers, have responsibility for delivery of FSA services at the state and county level.

The USDA focal point for coordination of emergency planning and response activities, including antiterrorism activities, is the Office of Crisis Planning and Management (OCPM) under the Assistant Secretary for Administration.[146] The OCPM program coordinates USDA participation in the Federal Response Plan, described above, and is the department's principal contact with FEMA and other Federal departments and agencies that have emergency responsibilities. The program operates through Headquarters Agency Emergency Contacts in the 50 states, Puerto Rico, and the Virgin Islands.

The Department of Agriculture has mandated responsibilities and substantial existing expertise, programs, and mechanisms in place to protect the Nation's food and agriculture infrastructure. These capabilities and networks could readily be brought to bear on combating bioterrorism because they extend to the grassroots level in virtually every county of the United States. As with natural outbreaks of livestock and crop diseases or food contamination, biological attacks will not be immediately apparent; therefore, existing frameworks for detecting, identifying, reporting, tracking, and managing disease outbreaks will have to be applied to combating agricultural bioterrorism, and appropriate responses will be formulated based on the specific pathogen, target organism, and other circumstances surrounding the attack. The key is to develop a well-coordinated strategy that leverages—to the maximum extent possible—relevant programs, capabilities, and resources across the department and Federal Government.

USDA Actions to Date

Based on intelligence reports subsequent to the Gulf War and the breakup of the Soviet Union, USDA became aware that Iraq and the former Soviet Union had active biological warfare programs directed at animal and plant agriculture and that American agricultural and food supplies were potential targets of bioweapons developed by these nations and other hostile actors. Consequently, USDA has undertaken several actions to address this threat.[147] For instance, USDA has worked closely with intelligence agencies, including through temporary person-nel details and mutually developed briefings, to clarify the extent of the threat and to expand awareness of the threat among Federal agencies and the general public. In addition, an ad hoc interagency working group has been established, with representatives from the USDA, CIA, DIA, and FBI.[148]

A USDA interagency committee has developed a preliminary plan to provide leadership to protect the Nation's food and agriculture against terrorism. Key goals of the plan are to prevent and deter terror-ism within the United States and against its interests abroad; maximize international cooperation to combat terrorism; improve domestic crisis and consequence planning and management; safeguard public safety and protect agriculture and the Nation's food supply; safeguard critical infra-structures in agriculture and the Nation's food supply system; and con-duct research to enhance counterterrorism capabilities. Furthermore, USDA participates in the NSC counterterrorism structure established by PDD 62. The department chairs a subgroup on Agriculture and Food Safety under the NSC Weapons of Mass Destruction Preparedness Group. It also has established collaborative research programs with for-mer Soviet scientists who were involved in the Soviet bioweapons pro-grams. The collaborative research is funded by the Department of State's Biotechnology Collaborative Research Program under the Freedom Sup-port Act. The program is a threat reduction initiative designed to pro-vide appropriate and rewarding research opportunities to unemployed former Soviet scientists whose expertise could be directed against the United States.

In June 1999, USDA Secretary Dan Glickman established a Counterterrorism Policy Council chaired by Deputy Secretary Richard Rominger and co-chaired by Catherine Woteki, Under Secretary for Food Safety. The council serves as the USDA senior policy forum to co-ordinate and leverage USDA-wide counterterrorism efforts. The Agricul-tural Research Service developed a proposal for a $391 million funding initiative for FY 2001 for research to enhance the capabilities of U.S. agriculture to prevent, respond to, and mitigate terrorist events.[149] The initiative included $214 million to upgrade ARS animal biocontainment facilities at the Plum Island Animal Disease Center; the Southeast Poul-try Research Facility; and the Arthropod-Borne Diseases Research Labo-ratory (A–B DRL). Unfortunately, only $500,000 was appropriated to ARS for counterterrorism research initiatives.[150]

Building a Strategy

The Department of Agriculture has an important opportunity to build on promising actions to date and capitalize on relevant programs and capabilities by providing strong leadership for a coordinated national strategy to combat agricultural bioterrorism, involving public and private customers, stakeholders, and partners at the Federal, state, and local levels. A comprehensive national plan to combat the threat of bioterrorism against U.S. food and agriculture must identify actions to prevent acts of terrorism in the first place and to respond to such acts if and when they do occur. Required actions cut across mission areas and capabilities of multiple Federal, state, and local agencies and organizations, and include the following measures:

Preventive Measures

- intelligence programs (identify potential threats and perpetrators; understand motivations; predict behavior; and consider preemptive action)
- monitoring programs (detect and track specific pathogens and diseases)
- targeted research (see appendix B for a description of high-priority counterterrorism research needs identified by ARS)
- moral suasion (discourage use of biological weapons)
- international treaties, protocols, and agreements (including effective verification programs)
- first-strike-deterrence strategies
- creation of agent-specific resistance in livestock, poultry, and crops
- vaccination against specific biological weapons agents
- modification, as appropriate, of vulnerable U.S. food and agriculture practices to minimize impacts of terrorist acts
- education and training of Federal, state, and local agencies in emergency drills
- public awareness via education programs.

Response Measures

- consequence management (also included in several of the following actions)
- early detection and prediction of patterns of dispersion
- early detection of specific biological weapons agents, delivery mechanisms, origins, and targets

- early management to check spread and minimize infection
- epidemiology
- treatment regimes
- casualty management (including carcass disposal and decontamination)
- diplomatic responses
- military responses
- legal responses
- economic responses
- compensation for losses
- management of economic consequences (including disruption of exports and commodity markets)
- education and training of Federal, state, and local agencies in emergency drills
- public awareness via education programs.

The strategic plan should provide a detailed action plan for each of these courses of action and a program for implementation, including time frame, milestones, specific responsibilities of involved organizations and interests, mechanisms for coordination and partnerships, budgetary requirements, and accountability mechanisms, including appropriate metrics to determine progress and success.

Key Issues to Address

In addition to identifying key actions to be undertaken in each of the areas listed above, the strategic plan should address several additional critical issues. These include linking or incorporating plan elements into the agency- and department-wide strategic plans required by the Government Performance and Review Act; defining roles and responsibilities of the private sector, including the agribusiness sector, to implement components of the plan; creating public awareness through education; and building a strong case for funding.

Leveraging and Coordinating USDA Programs

It is essential that, at the outset, the Secretary of Agriculture issue a strong and clear mandate to USDA agency heads, including specific leadership responsibilities for development of the strategic plan. The Department of Agriculture should ensure full involvement of all departmental agencies that can contribute to efforts to combat agricultural bioterrorism. The department should identify specific roles and responsibilities for all agencies, coordination mechanisms, and budgetary requirements.

Strategic Partnerships

While USDA should provide Federal leadership for a national strategy to counter agricultural bioterrorism, the department does not possess sufficient resources or the requisite range of responsibilities and capabilities to develop and implement the strategy. Instead, it must rely on strategic partnerships to accomplish this goal. A plethora of public and private organizations at the Federal, state, and local levels have responsibilities or capabilities related to protecting the Nation's food supplies. Building strategic partnerships with these interests will stimulate buy-in to the plan, facilitate consideration of different perspectives, leverage resources and capabilities across agencies, and help define specific roles and responsibilities of different organizations and agencies, thereby reducing program duplication and improving coordination.

Other Federal Agencies

Partnerships with other Federal agencies are desirable for two principal reasons: to address gaps in a comprehensive counterterrorism strategy, which are not within the USDA mission areas or range of capabilities, and to leverage capabilities in other Federal agencies with capabilities already existing in USDA. With reference to gaps, there are three major functional areas where the lack of requisite mission or expertise in USDA requires that these functions be performed by other agencies, in close communication with USDA. The first is intelligence, which is properly the primary responsibility of Federal intelligence agencies, including the CIA, DIA, armed services intelligence branches, and FBI. Timely, accurate, properly evaluated, and secure intelligence is critical to deterring bioterrorism. It is equally important that relevant intelligence information be shared with USDA officials quickly enough to be useful; however, because USDA has limited experience working with intelligence agencies, and relatively few employees with security clearances, building effective partnerships between USDA and intelligence agencies will be a challenging undertaking.

The second major gap is in the area of law enforcement and criminal proceedings. The USDA Office of Inspector General has responsibilities and capabilities to investigate threatened or actual criminal actions against U.S. food and agriculture. The FDA Office of Criminal Investigations has similar responsibilities. However, law enforcement is clearly the principal responsibility of the FBI, state and local law enforcement agents, and the courts. The key to effective partnerships between USDA and these entities is good communication, both at the local level and between the USDA Office of Inspector General and the Department of Justice.

The third important gap area is international relations and diplomacy. Although the USDA Foreign Agricultural Service (FAS) has some experience and capability in this area, with FAS personnel located in U.S. Embassies in many countries, this is the principal responsibility of the Department of State with support from U.S. intelligence agencies.

In addition to filling gaps in strategy, USDA should build strategic partnerships with other Federal agencies to leverage better its in-house capabilities and resources with related capabilities in other agencies and to enhance coordination of programs across agencies. There are five principal areas where this applies: research; detection, identification, and monitoring of biological agents and epidemiology; disease containment, including development and application of vaccines, therapeutics, and other treatments; consequence management, including disaster relief, financial relief, and cleanup and restoration of affected areas; education, training, and communications. Appendix C provides a framework for Federal agencies and programs that could complement USDA capabilities in these areas.

There are numerous examples of existing, successful collaboration between USDA and other Federal agencies in efforts that could contribute to counterterrorism. Key examples include the cooperative and collocated animal disease research programs of ARS and the U.S. Army Medical Research Institute for Infectious Diseases in Fort Detrick, Maryland (APHIS is also a partner), and the cooperative efforts between USDA and HHS in the area of food safety. In recent testimony before the Subcommittee on Emerging Threats, Senate Committee on Armed Services, Robert J. Newberry, Deputy Assistant Secretary of Defense for Combating Terrorism Policy and Support, identified several areas in which DOD and USDA have cooperated in efforts to combat agricultural bioterrorism.[151]

Nonetheless, there is a significant opportunity to expand these partnerships, to improve coordination among agency programs with similar missions and capabilities, and to target more effectively Federal resources and capabilities to support efforts to combat agricultural bioterrorism. For example, there are substantial capabilities in the Centers for Disease Control in human disease detection and diagnosis, as well as in epidemiology, that could be brought to bear on animal diseases. There is also an opportunity for expanded collaboration between ARS, APHIS, and the Department of the Interior National Wildlife

Health Center (NHWC) in monitoring diseases of domestic animals and wildlife. NHWC has been working closely with HHS in disease diagnosis and tracking and public education related to the recent outbreak of West Nile virus in New York. The DOD Defense Advanced Research Projects Agency (DARPA) could support research to combat agricultural bioterrorism. Reportedly, DARPA does not currently have the authority to conduct agriculture-related research.[152]

State and Local Government Agencies

Because the primary responsibility for preventing and responding to acts of terrorism in the United States lies with local and state authorities, the strategic plan must address coordination and partnerships between the Federal Government agencies and those authorities. This will be facilitated greatly by the strong linkages between USDA and the state and local agriculture interests through agricultural cooperative extension programs, Farm Service Agency offices, land-grant universities, and state departments of agriculture. However, USDA will be challenged to build partnerships with state and local authorities—including public health agencies—with which it has limited experience. It will be important to work closely with other Federal agencies—such as HHS—that have closer ties to these authorities.

Private Sector

In many ways, the most important partnerships will be with the private sector, particularly with the agribusiness sector—the most likely target of a terrorist act. Active involvement of the private sector in developing and implementing the strategy will generate buy-in to the strategy, help build support for funding initiatives, and provide additional capabilities, communications networks, and site-specific disease monitoring and tracking opportunities. Most important, the private sector will ultimately be responsible for developing and implementing biosecurity measures to protect farms and agribusiness interests from acts of terrorism or to remediate the effects of terrorism if it should occur. Public-private partnerships will be essential to identify, encourage, and fund actions to deter terrorism—including improved security on farms and in businesses, revised management procedures, pathogen identification and monitoring programs, information networks, and large-scale vaccination efforts—and to manage the consequences of terrorist acts. It is encouraging to note, in the wake of the September 11 attacks, that the American Farm Bureau Federation, the Nation's largest farm group, urged the Bush administration to appoint an agriculture specialist to serve in the new Office of Homeland Security.[153]

Key components of the private sector that must be involved include producers of crops, livestock, poultry, and aquaculture products. While it will be important to engage key companies possessing strategic market shares, the most effective approach will be to work with national commodity organizations that represent the broad interests of their constituencies, that have staff in place, and that are often involved in government affairs and lobbying activities. Examples of organizations representing key commodities include the American Soybean Association, National Cattlemen's Beef Association, American Poultry Association, American Sheep Industry Association, Catfish Farmers of America, National Corn Growers Association, National Cotton Foundation, National Livestock Producers Association, National Milk Producers Federation, and National Pork Producers Council. It will also be important to involve other agribusiness concerns, including major agribusiness companies, other trade organizations, food wholesalers and retailers, restaurants, slaughterhouses, processors, packagers, the transportation sector, feed companies, seed companies, other suppliers to the industry, and equipment manufacturers.

Other important private sector partners include the private research community, including universities (researchers from public universities and government laboratories must also be involved), private research organizations, and research divisions in agribusiness firms; professional organizations such as the American Agricultural Economics Association, American Society of Agricultural Engineers, American Society of Agronomy, American Society of Animal Science, U.S. Animal Health Association, American Association of Veterinary Laboratory Diagnosticians, and American Veterinary Medical Association; consumer and environmental organizations; and international organizations. A comprehensive listing of potential private sector partner organizations is presented in appendix E.

Chapter Four

Recommendations and Conclusion

Prior to initiating development of a coordinated national strategy to combat agricultural bioterrorism, USDA must identify critical needs of such a strategy and give careful thought to an effective approach to its development. This paper provides a number of separate recommendations for Federal actions, as follows:

Clear, well-coordinated Federal interagency mechanisms must be established for gathering, assessing, and sharing sensitive intelligence information on terrorist threats to U.S. food and agriculture. The information must be relevant and timely, while simultaneously ensuring security of classified data. Proposed mechanisms must be acceptable to intelligence agencies.

There should be a significant expansion of research capabilities related to animal or plant health and food safety, as well as a program focus on agricultural bioterrorism, even as it is recognized that expanded research in this area will benefit efforts in both food safety and the health of livestock, poultry, and crops. The principal target of increased funding should be USDA laboratories and programs. Expanded funding should be provided for intramural research in ARS laboratories, extramural research in universities and private laboratories through CSREES (via major research programs such as the National Research Initiative), and upgrading of laboratory facilities (see appendix B for relevant ARS research funding needs).

Substantial funding should be provided to upgrade ARS and APHIS biocontainment facilities, particularly at A–B DRL, Laramie, Wyoming; FADDL and PIADC, Plum Island, New York; NADC and NVSL, Ames, Iowa, and the Southeast Poultry Research Laboratory, Athens, Georgia. USDA presently has no biosafety level (BSL) 4 facilities. BSL 4 facilities are required for research on pathogens that confer highly contagious, hot diseases, including the animal diseases Bovine Spongiform Encephalopathy, as well as Hendrah and Nipah viruses.[154] An expanded research initiative should also include economics research, coordinated by ERS. It is also important to expand research related to agricultural bioterrorism in non-USDA agencies with relevant capabilities or responsibilities, including FDA, the Centers for Disease Control (CDC), U.S. Army Medical Research Institute for Infectious Diseases, and DARPA. As noted earlier, DARPA does not presently have the legislative authority to support agricultural research.[155]

Professional Federal staff in key areas must be expanded. For example, there is a critical shortage of qualified personnel in APHIS Veterinary Services who could readily respond to widespread disease epidemics that terrorists could initiate.[156] Well-coordinated interagency mechanisms must be established among the FBI, USDA, and DOD for collaborative forensics investigations. In particular, USDA specialized expertise in pathogens and diseases affecting agriculture must be effectively married to the FBI forensics capability to ensure that credible evidence can be gathered to support convictions of terrorists.[157]

CDC performance plans—"Public Health Response to Terrorism" and "Infectious Diseases"—should be considered for potential applicability to a national strategic plan to combat agricultural bioterrorism.[158] These CDC plans are incorporated into the overall Health and Human Services Strategic Plan required by the Government Performance and Results Act. The plans address the following Performance Measures related to bioterrorism:

- establish sentinel networks to identify early victims
- increase epidemiological, clinical, and laboratory capabilities of state and major city health departments
- establish a national, state-based network of reference laboratories to detect bioterrorist agents and provide rapid and accurate diagnosis
- provide training and technology transfer programs for state-of-the-art diagnostics for use in bioterrorism
- establish bioterrorism preparedness and response planning programs in states and localities
- expand electronic surveillance and communications systems in major metropolitan areas
- create a national pharmaceutical stockpile available for rapid deployment to areas impacted by bioterrorism.

Significantly, the Performance Measures related to bioterrorism either match or directly support those related to infectious diseases, and vice versa.

A considerable Federal program must be initiated to expand and locate the national supply of vaccines and pharmaceuticals to protect against or treat the most likely agricultural diseases launched by bioterrorists. The initiative should include research to improve or develop new vaccines and drugs (including effectiveness against a variety of agents and shelf life extension); manufacturing and strategic stockpiling; professional training; and assurance of a surge capability to expand manufacture and distribution in a crisis. A Federally-coordinated nationwide electronic communications and data management network also must be established that links the private agribusiness community with emergency management staff, field response personnel, and key Federal, state, and local agencies. This network could facilitate pathogen monitoring, reporting and tracking diseases, and communicating response measures and their effectiveness. Chalk has recommended establishment of "emergency management control centers" that could coordinate communications and data management.[159]

A national emergency disease response plan should be developed and implemented.[160] In 1996, the Animal and Plant Health Inspection Service established a Working Group on National Animal Health Emergency Management, with representatives from the Veterinary Services division of APHIS, the Animal Agriculture Coalition, the U.S. Animal Health Association, and the American Veterinary Medical Association.[161] This working group could be expanded to include APHIS Plant Protection and Quarantine representatives as well as key organizations and interests representing agricultural crops and could provide leadership for development of an agriculture emergency response plan. The USDA Food Safety and Inspection Service (FSIS) could initiate a similar program for bioterrorism targeting the food supply, building on existing frameworks such as the Food-borne Diseases Active Surveillance Network. This program, described above, is a collaborative effort of FSIS, FDA, CDC, state health departments, and local investigators to track food-borne illness throughout the United States. Emergency response plans should include provisions for training exercises with mock terrorist attacks.

Coordination must be improved and clear roles, responsibilities, expectations, and performance measures must be established for Federal, state, and local organizations and interests (both public and private) that will be involved in combating agricultural bioterrorism. Chalk has concluded that, at present, there is inadequate coordination between APHIS and state and local agencies involved in animal and plant health protection.[162] Clearly, there is an opportunity to improve coordination between USDA as a whole and all interests that could be affected by terrorist attacks against U.S. food and agriculture. It is particularly important to determine the appropriate roles and responsibilities of the private sector, vis-à-vis those of government agencies, in areas such as biosecurity; detection, diagnosis, tracking, and reporting of pathogens or disease outbreaks; disease containment and treatment procedures; and post-disease remediation.

Feasible options must be identified and investigated fully to provide financial assistance to agribusiness interests impacted by terrorism. For example, Chalk has suggested establishment of a national insurance plan "where a percentage of (agricultural) sales are held in reserve to help offset contingency costs in the event of a major or deliberate disease outbreak."[163] Also, a coordinated, interagency, Federally funded professional education and training program that is related to agricultural bioterrorism must be undertaken. The program should include focused professional education to train plant pathologists, veterinarians, and other first responders in the detection, identification, diagnosis, treatment, and containment of potential bioterrorist diseases and biosecurity training for agribusinesses.

In addition, a coordinated, interagency, Federally-funded public education and information initiative should be undertaken. Agriculture extension personnel and land-grant university educators should lead this effort. Public education and information programs must be carefully conceived and managed to raise public awareness without engendering public loss of confidence in the Nation's food supply. Stronger international cooperation should be encouraged to deter or respond to agricultural bioterrorism, including cooperative research and exchange programs; monitoring and identification of potential biological agents; and disease detection, tracking, and containment. For example, the Office International des Epizooties is a highly effective de facto "world animal health organization" that could include bioterrorism in its purview.[164] It is also important that international agricultural interests work to ensure both that agricultural bioterrorism gets attention in the effort to strengthen the international Biological Weapons Convention and that effective verification measures are developed and implemented for biological agents of concern to food and agriculture.

Sequential Approach for USDA Strategy Development

The Secretary of Agriculture appoints a small working group to develop the strategy. Michael Goldblatt, Deputy Director of Defense Sciences at DARPA, and a former director of research at McDonalds Corporation, has suggested that the development of the plan be an intense but low-profile effort.[165] In his opinion, it should be undertaken by a core working group of objective, highly credible, nonagency personnel (with no vested interests), with expertise in food and agriculture.[166] Key individuals from industry and both public and private organizations could serve as resource persons for the working group, which should have a strong mandate from the Secretary of Agriculture. It is important to emphasize that this group will fundamentally create a *Federal* strategy—that it not purport to tell state and local agencies, or the private agribusiness sector, what to do.

Assess threat and risk. The next step in developing the national strategy should be a thorough assessment of the threat and risk of agricultural bioterrorism. When persons with access to sensitive information regarding the threat are convinced that it is real and substantial, they may question the need for a threat and risk assessment to confirm the obvious.[167] On the other hand, the General Accounting Office has concluded that the absence of such an assessment has impeded development of a coordinated, effective, and appropriately focused strategy for combating bioterrorism in general.[168] An objective assessment of the threat and risk of agricultural bioterrorism, whether it provides substantial new information, will provide a solid and credible foundation for proposed counterterrorism actions and budget requests. The National Research Council (NRC) of the National Academy of Sciences should be tasked with conducting the assessment. An NRC report would assure objectivity and engender credibility with skeptical observers.

Frame the issue properly. Development of an effective strategy to combat agricultural bioterrorism is critically dependent on asking the right questions at the outset. Goldblatt believes that, to engage fully the agribusiness sector in counterterrorism activities, it is important to focus on broad, important issues affecting food and agriculture today.[169] Thus, he proposes that the following two questions be asked up front: What are the most important problems facing the food and agriculture industry today? How do we solve these problems in a way that simultaneously deters terrorism? Goldblatt suggests that the two most important problems are food safety and plant and animal diseases. Since agricultural bioterrorism is likely either to compromise food safety or to introduce catastrophic diseases, strategies to assure food safety or the health of crops and farm animals will simultaneously deter terrorism and engender support among customers and stakeholders.

Identify and involve key customers, stakeholders, and potential partners (public and private) in development of the strategy. These individuals could serve as resource personnel for the working group.

Review and evaluate related, relevant programs in other agencies and organizations. This issue was addressed above where it is recommended that CDC Performance Plans for "Public Health Response to Terrorism" and "Infectious Diseases" might be models for a USDA-led strategy. It is noteworthy that HHS in general, and CDC in particular, were initially slow in developing strategies to respond to bioterrorism but are now considered to be well on the way to developing highly effective interagency counterterrorism programs.[170]

Develop a white paper that lays out the key elements of the strategy for review and comment by stakeholders. It is important to take this step before developing a full strategic plan, not only to ensure that its proposed actions are feasible, complete, and acceptable, but also to help establish buy-in from key stakeholders. The white paper should be revised to address concerns and recommendations of the key stakeholders, then shared with the Secretary of Agriculture for review, comment, and approval.

Draft a complete strategic plan, including an implementation plan and timetable. Development of a full strategic plan, incorporating the elements of the white paper, should be the responsibility of USDA personnel, designated by the secretary, in cooperation with designated representatives of other Federal agencies with relevant capabilities, programs, and responsibilities. It is important that the strategic plan is consistent with and meshes well with the overall USDA strategic plan and individual USDA agency plans, as mandated by the Government Performance and Review Act. The plan should identify implementation actions, timetables for implementation, budget requirements, performance measures, and accountability mechanisms. The plan should address each of the Preventive Measures and Response Measures identified above, as well as roles and responsibilities, opportunities for strategic partnerships, and coordination issues.

Develop a budget. Paying for implementing the national strategy will be a significant challenge—perhaps the key issue in the entire process. It is particularly important that *new, sustained* funding be secured—to require agencies to reallocate existing budgets would inevitably affect performance in core mission areas. Securing funding for a new Federal program is difficult under any circumstances. Resources are invariably short, and competition among agencies and Congressional committees for control of scarce resources exacerbates the problem. The challenge to secure new funding to combat agricultural bioterrorism is especially daunting because agriculture is a relatively minor player in the national security establishment in general and in the counterterrorism arena in particular. To overcome this challenge, it is important that a budget to prevent and respond to agricultural bioterrorism be developed and presented as an interagency initiative. The proposed budget should identify appropriate levels of new funding for all Federal agencies that have roles to play in implementing the national strategy. It should also emphasize strategic partnerships among agencies that will reduce program overlap and duplication and effectively leverage appropriated resources. This approach will not only enhance collaboration among agencies but also encourage non-USDA agencies to champion the budget proposal. It is also important that key representatives of the agribusiness community strongly endorse the proposed budget. For example, the National Pork Producers Council has already identified the need for expanded research to deter agricultural bioterrorism as its highest research priority.[171]

Sell the plan. Once a draft of the strategic plan has been completed and accepted by the designated Federal team, it must be sold to the current administration (via the Office of Management and Budget) and to Congress. It will be important to enlist key, selected stakeholders in this effort to provide confidence that the proposed plan is acceptable to, and endorsed by, the agribusiness community and state and local organizations that will play a key role in plan implementation.

Conclusion

The consequences of a biological attack against U.S. food and agriculture could be devastating—in terms of both economic impact and the undermining of public confidence in the Nation's food supply. USDA should provide strong leadership for a coordinated Federal interagency strategy and program to combat agricultural biowarfare or bioterrorism. The strategy and program must address coordination and strategic partnerships with all agencies, organizations, and private interests that have relevant roles, responsibilities, or stakes in program outcomes. The program will not be cheap—an investment of several hundred million dollars is needed. However, given the potential risk and the fact that the United States is ill prepared to deter or respond to an attack, it cannot afford not to act.

An aggressive, well-coordinated effort to combat agricultural bioterrorism will have substantial ancillary benefits. Many antiterrorism actions could simultaneously help prevent or contain natural livestock and crop diseases, including a plethora of newly emerging diseases. Natural diseases cost U.S. agriculture billions of dollars annually. In addition, the effort could improve the safety of America's food, already an important national priority. Finally, this initiative will strengthen partnerships and improve coordination among agencies and organizations with responsibilities, programs, and capabilities to address a significant national threat. Perhaps, because the threat is more focused and manageable than other potential threats against the Nation's infrastructures, an effective, well-coordinated program may provide a model for other counterterrorism efforts.

Appendix A. Framework for National Coordination for Security, Critical Infrastructures, and Counterterrorism (lead agencies in parentheses; see appendix F for abbreviations)

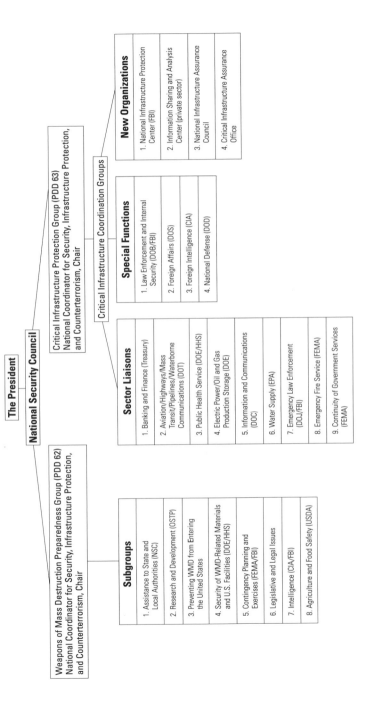

The President

National Security Council

Weapons of Mass Destruction Preparedness Group (PDD 62) National Coordinator for Security, Infrastructure Protection, and Counterterrorism, Chair

Critical Infrastructure Protection Group (PDD 63) National Coordinator for Security, Infrastructure Protection, and Counterterrorism, Chair

Critical Infrastructure Coordination Groups

Subgroups

1. Assistance to State and Local Authorities (NSC)
2. Research and Development (OSTP)
3. Preventing WMD from Entering the United States
4. Security of WMD-Related Materials and U.S. Facilities (DOE/HHS)
5. Contingency Planning and Exercises (FEMA/FBI)
6. Legislative and Legal Issues
7. Intelligence (CIA/FBI)
8. Agriculture and Food Safety (USDA)

Sector Liaisons

1. Banking and Finance (Treasury)
2. Aviation/Highways/Mass Transit/Pipelines/Waterborne Communications (DOT)
3. Public Health Service (DOE/HHS)
4. Electric Power/Oil and Gas Production Storage (DOE)
5. Information and Communications (DOC)
6. Water Supply (EPA)
7. Emergency Law Enforcement (DOJ/FBI)
8. Emergency Fire Service (FEMA)
9. Continuity of Government Services (FEMA)

Special Functions

1. Law Enforcement and Internal Security (DOB/FBI)
2. Foreign Affairs (DOS)
3. Foreign Intelligence (CIA)
4. National Defense (DOD)

New Organizations

1. National Infrastructure Protection Center (FBI)
2. Information Sharing and Analysis Center (private sector)
3. National Infrastructure Assurance Council
4. Critical Infrastructure Assurance Office

High-Priority Research Needs

The Agricultural Research Service has identified the following high-priority research needs to counter agricultural bioterrorism:

1. Expand on-the-spot diagnostic capabilities to include plant, animal, and insect threats
2. Conduct epidemiologic mapping of micro-organisms and pests to pinpoint geographical origins
3. Engineer and manufacture vaccines in the United States that are effective against all highly infectious disease agents of concern
4. Improve plant genetic resistance to potential introduced pathogens
5. Develop mass vaccine delivery systems for animals, poultry, and fish
6. Develop alternatives to widespread aerial chemical control of mosquitoes, midges, and other insect vectors of human, animal, and zoonotic disease
7. Conduct research to develop alternatives to malathion and other chemicals for control of insect pests or plants
8. Conduct research to prevent and control pathogens that are potential anticrop biological warfare weapons
9. Conduct research to identify genes that can enhance genetic resistance of major crops to pathogens that are potential biological warfare weapons
10. Develop innovative approaches to epidemic disease control
11. Conduct active research with foreign countries to clean up disease threats at the source and remove the natural sources of infectious agents and pests that terrorists or nations might easily access
12. Develop countertoxin technologies

Appendix C. Federal Agencies with Responsibilities (R), Programs (P), and Capabilities (C) that Directly Support Efforts to Counter Terrorism

Support area code:
1 Coordination
2 Intelligence
3 Crisis management, law enforcement, criminal investigations, and prosecution
4 Research
5 Agent detection, identification, and monitoring; epidemiology
6 Disease containment including development and application of vaccines, therapeutics, and other treatments
7 Consequence management (disaster relief; financial relief; cleanup; restoration)
8 Education and communications
9 International cooperation/relations

Agency/Program	1	2	3	4	5	6	7	8	9
Central Intelligence Agency		RPC							
Department of Agriculture									
Agricultural Marketing Service							C		
Animal and Plant Health Inspection Service			RPC		RPC	RPC	RPC	RPC	RPC
Agricultural Research Service				RPC					C
Cooperative State Research, Education and Extension Service				RPC					
Economic Research Service				RPC					
Forest Service	RPC							C	
Farm Services Agency								C	C
Food Safety and Inspection Service					RPC			RPC	RPC
Department of Defense									
Armed Forces Medical Intelligence Center		RPC							
Assistant Secretary of Defense for Special Operations and Low-Intensity Conflict	RPC								

Appendix C. Federal Agencies with Responsibilities (R), Programs (P), and Capabilities (C) that Directly Support Efforts to Counter Terrorism—*continued*

Support area code:
1 Coordination
2 Intelligence
3 Crisis management, law enforcement, criminal investigations, and prosecution
4 Research
5 Agent detection, identification, and monitoring; epidemiology
6 Disease containment including development and application of vaccines, therapeutics, and other treatments
7 Consequence management (disaster relief; financial relief, cleanup; restoration)
8 Education and communications
9 International cooperation/relations

Agency/Program	1	2	3	4	5	6	7	8	9
Department of Defense—continued									
Assistant to the Secretary of Defense for Civil Support	RPC								
U.S. Marines Chemical Biological Incident Response Force							RPC		
Defense Advanced Research Projects Agency				RPC					
Deputy Assistant Secretary of Defense for Combating Terrorism Policy and Support	RPC								
Defense Intelligence Agency		RPC							
Defense Threat Reduction Agency	RPC			RPC					
Chemical Biological-Rapid Response Team (Army)	RPC					RPC			RPC
Joint Program Office for Biological Defense	RPC								
Joint Task Force for Civil Support	RPC								
National Guard and Reserve Component						RPC	RPC	RPC	
U.S. Army Technical Escort Unit								RPC	
U.S. Army Medical Research Institute for Infectious Diseases					RPC	RPC			
U.S. Army Veterinary Service					RPC	RPC	RPC		

Agency/Program	Support area								
	1	2	3	4	5	6	7	8	9
Department of Energy									
Office of Emergency Preparedness	RPC								
Department of Health and Human Services									
Centers for Disease Control				RPC	RPC	RPC		RPC	
Food and Drug Administration				RPC		RPC		RPC	
National Institutes of Health				RPC		RPC			
Office of Emergency Preparedness–National Disaster Medical System	RPC					RPC	RPC		
Department of the Interior									
National Wildlife Health Center					RPC	RPC			RPC
Department of Justice									
Federal Bureau of Investigation		RPC	RPC						
Department of State									RPC
Environmental Protection Agency									
National Response Center/National Response Team	RPC							RPC	RPC
Federal Emergency Management Agency	RPC							RPC	RPC
National Security Council	RPC								
Office of Science and Technology Policy				RPC					
U.S. Customs			RPC	RPC					

Key Federal Programs and Capabilities to Combat Bioterrorism

1. Department of Defense, Under Secretary for Acquisition and Technology
2. Defense Advanced Research Projects Agency (Defense Sciences Directorate, Bio Warfare Defense Technologies Program; Special Projects Directorate, Biological Warfare Defense Systems Program)
3. Defense Threat Reduction Agency
4. Department of Defense, Secretary of the Army
5. Joint Program Office for Biological Defense (under Assistant Secretary for Acquisition, Logistics, and Technology)
6. U.S. Army Soldier and Biological Chemical Command (under U.S. Army Materiel Command)
7. U.S. Army Medical Research Institute of Infectious Diseases (under U.S. Army Medical Research and Materiel Command)
8. Department of Defense, United States Marine Corps, Chemical Biological Incident Response Force
9. Department of Defense National Guard and Reserve Components (several programs including National Guard military support detachments in each of 10 FEMA regions to assist state and local authorities in responding to WMD incidents. Initially called Rapid Assessment and Initial Detection [RAID] Teams, this designation is no longer used)
10. Department of Health and Human Services
11. Assistant Secretary for Health (Office of Public Health and Science; Surgeon General; U.S. Public Health Service; Office of Emergency Preparedness, including the National Disaster Medical System)
12. Food and Drug Administration
13. National Institutes of Health (National Institute of Environmental Health Sciences)

14. Centers for Disease Control and Prevention (National Center for Infectious Diseases; National Center for Environmental Health; Emergency Response Coordination Group)
15. Department of Agriculture (agriculture and food safety issues)
16. Under Secretary for Natural Resources and Environment (U.S. Forest Service)
17. Assistant Secretary for Administration (Disaster Management and Coordination staff)
18. Under Secretary for Research, Education, and Economics (Agricultural Research Service; Cooperative State Research Education and Extension Service; Economic Research Service)
19. Under Secretary for Food Safety (Food Safety and Inspection Service)
20. Under Secretary for Marketing and Regulatory Programs (Animal and Plant Health Inspection Service)
21. Federal Emergency Management Agency, Federal Response Plan

Selected Agricultural and Environmental Organizations

Farm Interest Organizations

Agrimerica (The Association for Agribusiness in America)
American Farm Bureau Federation
American Farmland Trust
Center for Agriculture and Rural Development
National Association of State Departments of Agriculture
National Council of Farm Cooperatives
National Future Farmers of America
Organic Farmers Marketing Association
Professional Farmers of America

Commodity Associations

Livestock, Poultry, and Fish

American Feed Industry Association
American Poultry Association
American Sheep Industry Association
Catfish Farmers of America
Livestock Marketing Association
National Aquaculture Association
National Cattlemen's Beef Association
National Contract Poultry Growers Association
National Honey Board
National Livestock Producers Association
National Milk Producers Federation
National Pork Producers Council

Crops

American Forage and Grassland Council
American Soybean Association
Fertilizer Institute
National Association of Wheat Growers
National Corn Growers Association
National Cotton Foundation
U.S. Feed Grains Council
U.S. Sugar Corporation

Agricultural Professional Societies

American Agricultural Economics Association
American Association of Avian Pathologists
American Association of Veterinary Laboratory Diagnosticians
American Crop Protection Association
American Chemical Society
American Dairy Science Association
American Phytopathological Society
American Registry of Professional Animal Scientists
American Society for Animal Science
American Society for Horticultural Science
American Society of Agricultural Consultants
American Society of Agricultural Engineers
American Society of Agronomy
Animal Agriculture Coalition
Animal Industry Foundation
Association of Applied Insect Ecologists
Association of Natural Biocontrol Producers
Coalition for Funding Agricultural Research Missions
Consortium for International Crop Protection
Council for Agricultural Science and Technology
Entomological Society of America
Equine Nutrition and Physiology Society
Federation of Animal Science Societies
International Embryo Transfer Society
National Alliance of Independent Crop Consultants
National Center for Agricultural Law Research and Information
National Mastitis Council

Poultry Science Association
Society of Nematologists
U.S. Animal Health Association
Weed Science Society of America

Environmental and Consumer Organizations

Agriculture for a Clean Environment
Environmental Defense Fund
Greenpeace
National Audubon Society
Sierra Club
Foundation E.A.R.T.H.
Herbicide Resistance Action Committee
Insecticide Resistance Action Committee
Kerr Center for Sustainable Agriculture, Inc.
National Institute for the Environment
People for the Ethical Treatment of Animals
Pesticide Action Network North America
Public Voice
Responsible Industry for a Sound Environment
Sustainable Agriculture Network

International Organizations

Consortium for International Crop Protection
Global Agricultural Biotechnology Association
Global Crop Protection Federation
Inter-American Institute for Cooperation on Agriculture
International Agribusiness Marketing and Trade
International Food Information Council
World Aquaculture Society
World Sustainable Agriculture Association

Acronyms

AFMIC	Armed Forces Medical Intelligence Center
AMS	Agricultural Marketing Service
APHIS	Animal and Plant Health Inspection Service
ARS	Agricultural Research Service
ASD SO/LIC	Assistant Secretary of Defense for Special Operations and Low-Intensity Conflict
ATSD–CS	Assistant to the Secretary of Defense for Civil Support
CBIRF	Chemical Biological Incident Response Force
CB–RRT	Chemical Biological-Rapid Response Team
CDC	Centers for Disease Control
CIA	Central Intelligence Agency
CSREES	Cooperative State Research, Education, and Extension Service
CTR Program	Cooperative Threat Reduction Program
DARPA	Defense Advanced Research Projects Agency
DASD CTP&S	Deputy Assistant Secretary of Defense for Combating Terrorism Policy and Support
DIA	Defense Intelligence Agency
DOC	Department of Commerce
DOD	Department of Defense
DOE	Department of Energy
DOJ	Department of Justice
DOS	Department of State
DOT	Department of Transportation
DTRA	Defense Threat Reduction Agency
EPA	Environmental Protection Agency
ERS	Economic Research Service

FBI	Federal Bureau of Investigation
FDA	Food and Drug Administration
FEMA	Federal Emergency Management Agency
FS	Forest Service
FSA	Farm Services Agency
FSIS	Food Safety and Inspection Service
HHS	Department of Health and Human Services
JPO–BD	Joint Program Office for Biological Defense
JTF–CS	Joint Task Force for Civil Support
NDMS	National Disaster Medical System
NG&RC	National Guard and Reserve Components
NIH	National Institutes of Health
NRC/NRT	National Response Center/National Response Team
NSC	National Security Council
NWHC	National Wildlife Health Center
OEP	Office of Emergency Preparedness
OSTP	Office of Science and Technology Policy
PPD	Presidential Decision Directive
RAID Team	Rapid Assessment and Initial Detection Team
SBCCOM	Soldier and Biological Chemical Command
TEU	Technical Escort Unit
USAMRIID	U.S. Army Medical Research Institute for Infectious Diseases
USAVS	U.S. Army Veterinary Service
USDA	U.S. Department of Agriculture

Endnotes

[1] General Accounting Office, "Combating Terrorism: Selected Challenges and Related Recommendations," report, September 20, 2001, GAO/NSIAD–01–822, accessed at <http://www.gao.gov>.

[2] See, for example, Philip H. Abelson, "Biological Warfare," *Science* 286, no. 5 (November 26, 1999), 1677; William J. Clinton, "Remarks at the National Academy of Sciences, January 22, 1999," *Weekly Compilation of Presidential Documents* 35, no. 3, 103–106; Lois R. Ember, "DARPA Expands R&D on Biowarfare Defense Tools," *Chemical and Engineering News* 76, no. 7 (February 16, 1998), 7; Sidney J. Freedberg, Marilyn W. Serafini, and Siobhan Gorman, "Be Afraid, Be Moderately Afraid," *National Journal* 31, no. 13 (March 27, 1999), 806–817; Donald A. Henderson, "The Looming Threat of Bioterrorism," *Science* 283, no. 5406 (February 26, 1999), 1279–1282; Milton Leitenberg, "Biological Weapons: A Reawakened Concern," *The World & I* 14, no. 1 (January 1999), 289–305; Glenn E. Schweitzer and Carole C. Dorsch, *Superterrorism: Assassins, Mobsters, and Weapons of Mass Destruction* (New York: Plenum Press, 1998); White House, White Paper: The Clinton Administration's Policy on Critical Infrastructure Protection: Presidential Decision Directive 63, May 22, 1998; White House, Fact Sheet: Preparedness for a Biological Weapons Attack, May 22, 1998, available at <http://www.nbcindustrygroup.com/0522pres1.htm>; White House, Fact Sheet: Combating Terrorism: Presidential Decision Directive 62, May 22, 1998, available at <http://www.nbcindustrygroup.com/0522pres3.htm>.

[3] White House, *A National Security Strategy for a New Century,* December 1999.

[4] Clinton, "Remarks at the National Academy of Sciences"; Lois R. Ember, "Bioterrorism: Countering the Threat," *Chemical Engineering News* 77, no. 27 (July 5, 1999), 8–17; Tom Mangold and Jeff Goldberg, *Plague Wars: The Terrifying Reality of Biological Warfare* (New York: St. Martin's Press, 2000).

[5] Ember, "Bioterrorism: Countering the Threat"; Freedberg, Serafini, and Gorman, "Be Afraid, Be Moderately Afraid"; Donald A. Henderson, "Weapons for the Future," *The Lancet* 354 (supplement, December 1999), S64.

[6] Norm Steele, 2000.

[7] General Accounting Office, "Food Safety: Agencies Should Further Test Plans for Responding to Deliberate Contamination," letter report, October 27, 1999, GAO/RCED–00–3, accessed at <http://frwebgate.access.gpo.gov>.

[8] General Accounting Office, "Combating Terrorism: Observations on Biological Terrorism and Public Health Initiatives," testimony, March 16, 1999, GAO/T–NSIDA–99–112, accessed at <http://frwebgate.access.gpo.gov>.

[9] Rebecca Hersman and W. Seth Carus, "DOD and Consequence Management: Mitigating the Effects of Chemical and Biological Attack," *Strategic Forum* no. 169, Institute for National Strategic Studies, National Defense University Press (December 1999).

[10] W. Seth Carus, "Bioterrorism and Biocrimes: The Illicit Use of Biological Agents in the 20th Century," Center for Counterproliferation Research, National Defense University (August 1998; rev. July 1999).

[11] General Accounting Office, "Combating Terrorism: Issues to Be Resolved to Improve Counterterrorism Operations," letter report, May 13, 1999, GAO/NSIAD–99–135, accessed at <http://frwebgate4.access.gpo.gov>.

[12] Advisory Panel to Assess Domestic Response Capabilities for Terrorism Involving Weapons of Mass Destruction, "First Annual Report to the President and the Congress, Part I: Assessing the Threat," December 15, 1999.

[13] Carus, "Bioterrorism and Biocrimes."

[14] Paul Rogers, Simon Whitby, and Malcolm Dando, "Biological Warfare Against Crops," *Scientific American* 280, no. 6 (June 1999), 70–75.

[15] Ronald E. Hurlbert, "Microbiology 101 Internet Text: Chapter XV, Addendum: Biological Weapons; Malignant Biology," accessed at <http://www.wsu.edu/~hurlbert/pages/101biological weapons.html>.

[16] Abelson, "Biological Warfare"; Ethirajan Anbarasan, "Genetic Weapons: A 21st Century Nightmare?" *The UNESCO Courier* 52, no. 3 (1999), 37–39; "Bioterrorism, Foodborne Diseases, and 'Superbugs' Pose New Threats to U.S. Cities," *PR Newswire* (October 6, 1998); Cultural Terrorist Agency, "Genetics Activists Create Superweed Kit" (January 24, 1999); Hurlbert, "Microbiology 101 Internet Text"; Mangold and Goldberg, *Plague Wars*; Richard Preston, "The Bioweaponeers," *The New Yorker* 74, no. 3 (March 9, 1998), 52.

[17] Mark G. Kortepeter and Gerald W. Parker, "Potential Biological Weapons Threats," *Emerging Infectious Diseases* 5, no. 4 (July/August 1999), available at <http://www.cdc.gov/ncidod/EID/vol5no4/kortepeter.htm>.

[18] Ibid.

[19] Ibid.

[20] Anbarasan, "Genetic Weapons: A 21st Century Nightmare?"; Philip Cohen, "A Terrifying Power," *New Scientist* 161, no. 2171 (January 30, 1999), 10; Lois R. Ember, "A Double-Edged Sword," *Chemical and Engineering News* 77, no. 49 (December 6, 1999), 109–117.

[21] Deb Riechmann, "Russian Lab Develops Anthrax Strain that Might Defeat U.S. Vaccine," The Associated Press, February 14, 1998.

[22] Christine M. Gosden, testimony before the Senate Judiciary Subcommittee on Technology, Terrorism, and Government and the Senate Select Committee on Intelligence on Chemical and Biological Weapons Threats to America, "Are We Prepared?" April 22, 1998.

[23] Preston, "The Bioweaponeers."

[24] Hurlbert, "Microbiology 101 Internet Text"; Kortepeter and Parker, "Potential Biological Weapons Threats."

[25] Cited in W. Seth Carus, "Biological Warfare Threats in Perspective," *Critical Reviews in Microbiology* 24, no. 3 (1998), 149–155.

[26] Ibid.; Peter Chalk, unpublished review of agricultural bioterrorism, The RAND Corporation, 1999; Robert P. Kadlec, "Biological Weapons for Waging Economic Warfare," in *Battlefield of the Future: 21st Century Warfare Issues*, eds. Barry R. Schneider and Lawrence E. Grinter (Maxwell AFB, AL: Air University Press, 1995).

[27] Kortepeter and Parker, "Potential Biological Weapons Threats."

[28] Cited in Carus, "Biological Warfare Threats in Perspective"; Carus, "Bioterrorism and Biocrimes"; Freedberg, Serafini, and Gorman, "Be Afraid, Be Moderately Afraid"; Robert P. Kadlec, "Twenty-First Century Germ Warfare," in *Battlefield of the Future: 21st Century Warfare Issues*; Hurlbert, "Microbiology 101 Internet Text"; Al J. Venter, "New-Era Threat: Iraq's Biological Weapons," *Middle East Policy* 6, no. 4 (June 1999), 104–117.

[29] Terry N. Mayer, "The Biological Weapon: A Poor Nation's Weapon of Mass Destruction," in *Battlefield of the Future: 21st Century Warfare Issues*, 205–226.

[30] Hurlbert, "Microbiology 101 Internet Text."

[31] Freedberg, Serafini, and Gorman, "Be Afraid, Be Moderately Afraid."

[32] Federation of American Scientists, Working Group on Biological Weapons Verification, Report of the Subgroup on Investigation of Alleged Release of Biological or Toxin Weapons Agents (April 1996).

[33] W. Seth Carus, testimony before a joint hearing of the Senate Select Committee on Intelligence and the Senate Judiciary Committee Subcommittee on Technology, Terrorism, and Government Information, Washington, DC (March 4, 1998).

[34] Ibid.; Kadlec, "Twenty-First Century Germ Warfare."

[35] Richard Preston, "Taming the Biological Beast," *The New York Times*, April 21, 1998, 21.

[36] Ember, "Bioterrorism: Countering the Threat"; Freedberg, Serafini, and Gorman, "Be Afraid, Be Moderately Afraid"; Laurie Garrett, *The Coming Plague: Newly Emerging Diseases in a World out of Balance* (New York: Farrar Straus Giroux, 1994).

[37] Freedberg, Serafini, and Gorman, "Be Afraid, Be Moderately Afraid."

[38] Norm Steele, personal communication, March 22, May 24, 2000.

[39] Carus, testimony, March 4, 1998; Hurlbert, "Microbiology 101 Internet Text."

[40] Michael Heylin, "Ag Biotech's Promise Clouded by Consumer Fear," *Chemical and Engineering News* 77, no. 49 (December 6, 1999), 73–88.

[41] Hurlbert, "Microbiology 101 Internet Text."

[42] W. Seth Carus, "The Threat of Bioterrorism," *Strategic Forum* no. 127, Institute for National Strategic Studies, National Defense University Press (September 1997).

[43] USDA, Advisory Committee on Agricultural Biotechnology, Federal Register Notice 64, no. 108 (June 7, 1999), 30297; "Man Who Poisoned Food Gets 11-Year Jail Term," *The Boston Globe,* September 24, 1999, A16; Chalk, unpublished review; Steve Goldstein, "U.S. Could Face New Terror Tactic: Agricultural Warfare," *The Philadelphia Inquirer,* June 22, 1999; Siobhan Gorman, "Bioterror Down on the Farm," *National Journal* 31, no. 13 (March 27, 1999), 812–813; Debora MacKenzie, "Run, Radish, Run," *New Scientist* 164, no. 2217 (December 18, 1999), 36–39; Rogers, Whitby, and Dando, "Biological Warfare Against Crops."

[44] General Accounting Office, "Combating Terrorism: Observations on Biological Terrorism and Public Health Initiatives"; General Accounting Office, "Combating Terrorism: Need for Comprehensive Threat and Risk Assessments of Chemical and Biological Attacks," letter report, September 7, 1999, GAO/NSIAD–99–163, accessed at <http://frwebgate.access.gpo.gov>; General Accounting Office, "Observations on the Threat of Chemical and Biological Terrorism," testimony, October 20, 1999, GAO/T–NSIAD–00–50, accessed at <http://frwebgate.access.gpo.gov>.

[45] General Accounting Office, "U.S. Agriculture: Status of the Farm Sector," fact sheet for Congressional committees, GAO/RCED–95–104FS, March 1995.

[46] USDA, Agricultural Research Service, "Econoterrorism, a.k.a. Agricultural Bioterrorism or Asymmetric Use of Biological Weapons," unclassified briefing, February 28, 2000; Terrance M. Wilson et al., "A Review of Agroterrorism, Biological Crimes, and Biological Warfare Targeting Animal Agriculture," draft manuscript.

[47] USDA, Agricultural Research Service, "Econoterrorism."

[48] USDA, Advisory Committee on Agricultural Biotechnology, Federal Register Notice 64; USDA, Foreign Agricultural Service, "Selected Farm Products—United States and World Production and Exports: 1995 to 1998," Foreign Agricultural Commodity Circular Series, no. 1124, 1999.

[49] General Accounting Office, "U.S. Agriculture: Status of the Farm Sector."

[50] USDA, Advisory Committee on Agricultural Biotechnology, Federal Register Notice 64; USDA, Foreign Agricultural Service, "Selected Farm Products."

[51] Wilson et al., "A Review of Agroterrorism, Biological Crimes, and Biological Warfare Targeting Animal Agriculture."

[52] Norm Steele, "Econoterrorism: U.S. Agricultural Productivity, Concentration, and Vulnerability to Biological Weapons," unclassified Defense Intelligence Assessment for the DOD Futures Intelligence Program, January 14, 2000.

[53] Ibid.

[54] Chalk, unpublished review.

[55] USDA, Advisory Committee on Agricultural Biotechnology, Federal Register Notice 64.

[56] Gorman, "Bioterror Down on the Farm."

[57] Chalk, unpublished review; Goldstein, "U.S. Could Face New Terror Tactic"; Gorman, "Bioterror Down on the Farm."

[58] USDA, Agricultural Research Service, "Econoterrorism."

[59] USDA, Advisory Committee on Agricultural Biotechnology, Federal Register Notice 64; Chalk, unpublished review.

[60] Michael Goldblatt, personal communication, April 6, 2000.

[61] Ibid.

[62] Chalk, unpublished review.

[63] "Terrorists on the Green," *Discover* 20, no. 11 (1999), 30; Chalk, unpublished review; Rogers, Whitby, and Dando, "Biological Warfare Against Crops."

[64] Chalk, unpublished review; Goldstein, "U.S. Could Face New Terror Tactic."

[65] Chalk, unpublished review.

[66] Ibid.

[67] Cultural Terrorist Agency, "Genetics Activists Create Superweed Kit."

[68] MacKenzie, "Run, Radish, Run."

[69] Chalk, unpublished review; Rogers, Whitby, and Dando, "Biological Warfare Against Crops."

[70] Chalk, unpublished review.

[71] Advisory Panel to Assess Domestic Response Capabilities for Terrorism Involving Weapons of Mass Destruction, "First Annual Report to the President and the Congress, Part I: Assessing the Threat," December 15, 1999; Chalk, unpublished review; MacKenzie, "Run, Radish, Run."

[72] Chalk, unpublished review.

[73] Advisory Panel to Assess Domestic Response Capabilities for Terrorism Involving Weapons of Mass Destruction, "First Annual Report"; Chalk, unpublished review; Goldstein, "U.S. Could Face New Terror Tactic."

[74] Wilson et al., "A Review of Agroterrorism, Biological Crimes, and Biological Warfare Targeting Animal Agriculture."

[75] Chalk, unpublished review; Goldstein, "U.S. Could Face New Terror Tactic"; Kadlec, "Biological Weapons for Waging Economic Warfare"; MacKenzie, "Run, Radish, Run"; Judith Miller, "U.S. to Use Lab for More Study of Bioterrorism," *The New York Times,* September 22, 1999, A1, A25; Rogers, Whitby, and Dando, "Biological Warfare Against Crops"; Wilson et al. "A Review of Agroterrorism, Biological Crimes, and Biological Warfare Targeting Animal Agriculture"; Tabassum Zakaria, "Soviet Era Bugs Threaten U.S. Farming," *The Times of India,* September 16, 1999.

[76] Steele, "Econoterrorism: U.S. Agricultural Productivity, Concentration, and Vulnerability to Biological Weapons."

[77] Chalk, unpublished review.

[78] Floyd P. Horn and Roger G. Breeze, "Agriculture and Food Security," in *Food and Agricultural Security: Guarding against Natural Threats and Terrorist Attacks Affecting Health, National Food Supplies, and Agricultural Economics,* eds. Thomas W. Frazier and Drew C. Richardson, *Annals of the New York Academy of Natural Sciences* 894 (New York: New York Academy of Sciences, 1999), 9–17.

[79] Defense Intelligence Agency, "The Worldwide Agricultural Biological Warfare Threat," unclassified briefing, Biological Warfare Division, Office for Counterproliferation Support, 2000; Goldstein, "U.S. Could Face New Terror Tactic"; Grant Robertson, "Crop Warfare Combat Plan Urged," *Calgary Herald,* August 21, 1999; USDA, Agricultural Research Service, "Econoterrorism"; Wilson et al., "A Review of Agroterrorism, Biological Crimes, and Biological Warfare Targeting Animal Agriculture."

[80] Chalk, unpublished review; Goldstein, "U.S. Could Face New Terror Tactic."

[81] Wilson et al., "A Review of Agroterrorism, Biological Crimes, and Biological Warfare Targeting Animal Agriculture."

[82] Horn and Breeze, "Agriculture and Food Security."

[83] Ibid.

[84] Wilson et al., "A Review of Agroterrorism, Biological Crimes, and Biological Warfare Targeting Animal Agriculture."

[85] USDA, Agricultural Research Service, "Econoterrorism."

[86] Ibid.

[87] Hurlbert, "Microbiology 101 Internet Text."

[88] Wilson et al., "A Review of Agroterrorism, Biological Crimes, and Biological Warfare Targeting Animal Agriculture."

[89] Ronald M. Atlas, "Combating the Threat of Biowarfare and Bioterrorism," *Bioscience* 49, no. 6 (June 1999), 465–467; George W. Christopher et al., "Biological Warfare: A Historical Perspective," *Journal of the American Medical Association* 278, no. 5 (August 6, 1997), 412–417; Mayer, "The Biological Weapon: A Poor Nation's Weapon of Mass Destruction."

[90] Carus, "Bioterrorism and Biocrimes."

[91] Jonathan B. Tucker, "Historical Trends Related to Bioterrorism: An Empirical Analysis," *Emerging Infectious Diseases* 5, no. 4 (July/August 1999), available at <http://www.cdc.gov/ncidod/EID/vol5no4/tucker.htm>.

[92] J.B. Orenstein, "Now Fear This," *The Washington Post,* December 26, 1999, B1.

[93] Alliance for America, "Bombings of Two USDA Facilities in Washington State," memorandum, July 7, 1998; Alliance for America, "Congress Holds Hearings on Eco-Terror," memorandum, July 7,

1998; "Agriculture Fears Terrorist Threats to Food Supply," *Department of Energy and Nuclear Regulatory Commission Monthly Terrorism and Security Report* 3, no. 10 (October 1999); National Animal Interest Alliance, Request for Action by the Senate Judiciary Committee of the Congress of the United States: Animal Experts Representing Livestock Production, Farming, Science and Pets to Petition U.S. Senate to Focus on Terrorism, 1999, available at <http://www.naiaonline.org>; National Animal Interest Alliance, "Terrorism Gains Momentum: Animal Rights and Environmental Criminals Use Violence to Achieve Their Ends," 1999, available at <http://www.naiaonline.org/body/ articles/archives/arterror.htm>; G. Davidson Smith, "Single Issue Terrorism," *Canadian Security Intelligence Service, Commentary* no. 74 (Winter 1998).

[94] U.S. Department of Justice, "Report to Congress on the Extent of Domestic and International Terrorism in Animal Enterprises," September 2, 1993.

[95] National Animal Interest Alliance, "Terrorism Gains Momentum."

[96] Scott R. Taylor, Amy M. Rowe, and Brian M. Lewis, "Consequence Management—In Need of a Timeout," *Joint Force Quarterly* 22 (Summer 1999), 78–85.

[97] Federal Emergency Management Agency, "Backgrounder: Terrorism," available at <http:// www.fema.gov/library/terror.htm>.

[98] General Accounting Office, "Combating Terrorism: FBI's Use of Federal Funds for Counterterrorism-Related Activities (Fiscal Years 1995–1998)," letter report, November 20, 1998, GAO/GGD–99–7, accessed at <http://frwebgate.access.gpo.gov>; Hersman and Carus, "DOD and Consequence Management."

[99] Advisory Panel to Assess Domestic Response Capabilities for Terrorism Involving Weapons of Mass Destruction, "First Annual Report to the President and the Congress, Part I: Assessing the Threat," December 15, 1999, appendix A.

[100] Ibid.

[101] Hersman and Carus, "DOD and Consequence Management."

[102] Ibid.

[103] Center for Nonproliferation Studies, "Federal Funding to Combat Terrorism," available at <http://www.cns.miis.edu/research/cbw/terfund.htm>; General Accounting Office, "Observations on Federal Spending to Combat Terrorism," testimony, March 11, 1999, GAO/T–NSIAD/GGD–99–107, accessed at <http://frwebgate.access.gpo.gov>.

[104] Center for Nonproliferation Studies, "Federal Funding to Combat Terrorism."

[105] Advisory Panel to Assess Domestic Response Capabilities for Terrorism Involving Weapons of Mass Destruction, "First Annual Report to the President and the Congress, Part I: Assessing the Threat," December 15, 1999; "Terrorism 2000," *Current Events* 97, no. 24 (1998), 2a–2d; Commission to Assess the Organization of the Federal Government to Combat the Proliferation of Weapons of Mass Destruction, "Combating Proliferation of Weapons of Mass Destruction," report to the U.S. Senate, July 14, 1999; Jessica K. Drake, "After All These Years: Chem-Bio Defense Unequal to Threat," *National Defense* 83, no. 543 (December 1998), 39; John Elvin, "Bioterrorism Breeds a Growth Industry," *Insight on the News* 15, no. 45 (December 6, 1999), 35; Freedberg, Serafini, and Gorman, "Be Afraid, Be Moderately Afraid"; General Accounting Office, "Combating Terrorism: Observations on Biological Terrorism and Public Health Initiatives"; General Accounting Office, "Combating Terrorism: Observations on the Nunn-Lugar-Domenici Domestic Preparedness Program," testimony, October 2, 1998, GAO/T–NSIAD–99–16, accessed at <http://frwebgate.access.gpo.gov>; General Accounting Office, "Combating Terrorism: Opportunities to Improve Domestic Preparedness Program Focus and Efficiency," letter report, November 12, 1998, GAO/NSIAD–99–3, abstract accessed at <http://frwebgate4.access.gpo.gov>; General Accounting Office, "Combating Terrorism: Analysis of Potential Emergency Response Equipment and Sustainment Costs," letter report, June 9, 1999, GAO/NSIAD–99–151, accessed at <http://frwebgate.access.gpo.gov>; General Accounting Office, "Combating Terrorism: Need for Comprehensive Threat and Risk Assessments of Chemical and Biological Attacks"; General Accounting Office, "Combating Terrorism: Chemical and Biological Medical Supplies are Poorly Managed," letter report, October 29, 1999, GAO/HEHS/AIMD–00–36, abstract accessed at <http://frwebgate4.access.gpo.gov>.

[106] Taylor, Rowe, and Lewis, "Consequence Management—In Need of a Timeout."

[107] Ibid.

[108] Advisory Panel to Assess Domestic Response Capabilities for Terrorism Involving Weapons of Mass Destruction, "First Annual Report."

[109] General Accounting Office, "Combating Terrorism: Observations on the Nunn-Lugar-Domenici Domestic Preparedness Program"; General Accounting Office, "Combating Terrorism: Observations on the Growth of Federal Programs," testimony, June 9, 1999, GAO/T–NSIAD–99–181, accessed at <http://frwebgate.access.gpo.gov>.

[110] Advisory Panel to Assess Domestic Response Capabilities for Terrorism Involving Weapons of Mass Destruction, "First Annual Report."

[111] General Accounting Office, "Combating Terrorism: Opportunities to Improve Domestic Preparedness Program Focus and Efficiency"; General Accounting Office, "Observations on Federal Spending to Combat Terrorism."

[112] General Accounting Office, "Observations on Federal Spending to Combat Terrorism."

[113] General Accounting Office, "Combating Terrorism: Need for Comprehensive Threat and Risk Assessments of Chemical and Biological Attacks."

[114] Advisory Panel to Assess Domestic Response Capabilities for Terrorism Involving Weapons of Mass Destruction, "First Annual Report."

[115] Ibid.

[116] Ibid.

[117] Ibid.; General Accounting Office, "Combating Terrorism: Analysis of Potential Emergency Response Equipment and Sustainment Costs."

[118] General Accounting Office, "Observations on Federal Spending to Combat Terrorism."

[119] Advisory Panel to Assess Domestic Response Capabilities for Terrorism Involving Weapons of Mass Destruction, "First Annual Report."

[120] Hersman and Carus, "DOD and Consequence Management."

[121] Ibid.

[122] Chalk, unpublished review; Goldstein, "U.S. Could Face New Terror Tactic"; Gorman, "Bioterror Down on the Farm"; MacKenzie, "Run, Radish, Run"; Rogers, Whitby, and Dando, "Biological Warfare Against Crops"; Norm W. Schaad, "What Is an Effective Pathogen?" APSnet, Abstracts of the 1999 American Phytopathological Society Annual Meeting Symposium: Plant Pathology's Role in Anti-Crop Bioterrorism and Food Security (September 15–October 31, 1999), available at <http://www.apsnet.org/online/feature/BioSecurity/Top.html>.

[123] USDA, National Agricultural Statistics Service, "Agriculture—Farms, Acreage, and Foreign Trade: 1990 to 1998," no. 1441 (1999).

[124] The White House, White Paper: The Clinton Administration's Policy on Critical Infrastructure Protection.

[125] Advisory Panel to Assess Domestic Response Capabilities for Terrorism Involving Weapons of Mass Destruction, "First Annual Report."

[126] Floyd P. Horn, statement before the U.S. Senate Emerging Threats and Capabilities Subcommittee of the Armed Services Committee, October 27, 1999, available at <http://www.senate.gov/~armed_services/hearings/1999/e991027.htm>.

[127] Richard Chapman, *Chemical and Biological Warfare Primer,* Virtual Information Center, 2001, available at <http://www.vic-info.org>.

[128] Center for Nonproliferation Studies, "Federal Funding to Combat Terrorism."

[129] USDA, Advisory Committee on Agricultural Biotechnology, Federal Register Notice 64.

[130] Randall Murch, personal communication, April 17, 2000.

[131] USDA, Animal and Plant Health Inspection Service, "The Foreign Animal Disease Diagnostic Laboratory at Plum Island Animal Disease Center," December 1992, available at <http://www.aphis.usda.gov:80/oa/pubs/fsfadlab.html>; USDA, Agricultural Research Service, ". . . about the Research Center at Plum Island, New York," available at <http://www.arserrc.gov/naa/home/piadc.htm>.

[132] Louisiana Cooperative Extension Services, "Welcome to EDEN: Extension Disaster Education Network," accessed at <http://www.agctr.lso.edu/eden>.

[133] USDA, Animal and Plant Health Inspection Service, "Center for Animal Health Monitoring (CAHM): National Animal Health Monitoring System," available at <http://www.aphis.usda.gov/vs/ceah/cahm.htm>; USDA, Animal and Plant Health Inspection Service, "Facts about APHIS: Monitoring Plant and Animal Diseases," available at <http://www.aphis.usda.gov/oa/monitor.html>.

[134] USDA, Animal and Plant Health Inspection Service, "Emergency Programs: Keeping America Free from Foreign Animal Diseases," available at <http://www.aphis.usda.gov/oa/emergency.html>; Chalk, unpublished review.

[135] Ron Sequeira, "Safeguarding Production Agriculture and Natural Ecosystems against Biological Terrorism: A U.S. Department of Agriculture Emergency Response Framework," Frazier and Richardson, eds., 48–67; Anne Kohnen, "Responding to the Threat of Agroterrorism: Specific Recommendations for the USDA," BCSIA Discussion Paper 2000–29 and ESDP Discussion Paper ESDP–2000–04 (Cambridge, MA: Harvard University Press, 2000).

[136] Chalk, unpublished review.

[137] USDA, Animal and Plant Health Inspection Service, "The Foreign Animal Disease Diagnostic Laboratory at Plum Island Animal Disease Center."

[138] USDA, Animal and Plant Health Inspection Service, "Facts about APHIS: Monitoring Plant and Animal Diseases."

[139] USDA, Animal and Plant Health Inspection Service, "Facts about APHIS: Excluding Foreign Pests and Diseases," available at <http://www.aphis.usda.gov/oa/exclude.html>.

[140] USDA, Food Safety and Inspection Service, "Agriculture Fact Book 98: Chapter 9: Food Safety," available at <http://www.usda.gov/news/pubs/fbook98/chart9.htm>.

[141] Ibid.

[142] The program is described in detail at <http://www.fsis.usda.gov/ophs/fsisrep1.htm>.

[143] Bonnie Buntain and George Bickerton, "The U.S. Department of Agriculture Food Safety and Inspection Service's Activities in Assuring Biosecurity and Public Health Protection," in *Food and Agricultural Security: Guarding Against Natural Threats and Terrorist Attacks Affecting Health, National Food Supplies, and Agricultural Economics.*

[144] General Accounting Office, "Food Safety: Agencies Should Further Text Plans for Responding to Deliberate Contamination."

[145] Farm Service Agency *Online,* available at <http://www.fsa.usda.gov/pas/default.asp>.

[146] USDA, Office of Crisis Planning and Management, available at <http://www.usda.gov/da/ocpm>.

[147] Horn, statement before the United States Senate Emerging Threats and Capabilities Subcommittee of the Armed Services Committee.

[148] Chalk, unpublished review.

[149] USDA, Agricultural Research Service, "FY 2001 Agency Estimates: Enhancing the Capabilities of U.S. Agriculture to Prevent, Respond to, and Remediate Terrorist Events," 1999.

[150] Floyd P. Horn, personal communication, May 2, 2000.

[151] Robert J. Newberry, statement before the Senate Armed Services Committee, Subcommittee on Emerging Threats, October 27, 1999, available at <http://www.senate.gov/~armed_services/hearings/1999/e991027.htm>.

[152] Goldblatt, personal communication.

[153] Randy Fabi, "Boost Agriculture Security, Farm Groups Ask Bush," Reuters, October 2, 2001.

[154] Chalk, unpublished review.

[155] Goldblatt, personal communication.

[156] Chalk, unpublished review.

[157] Ibid.

[158] Centers for Disease Control and Prevention, "CDC Performance Plans, IV: Infectious Diseases," accessed at <http://www.cdc.gov/od/perfpln/2000iv.htm>; Centers for Disease Control and Prevention, "CDC Performance Plans, XIV: Public Health Response to Terrorism," accessed at <http://www.cdc.gov/od/perfpln/2000xiv.htm>.

[159] Chalk, unpublished review.

[160] Ibid.

[161] Ibid.

[162] Ibid.

[163] Ibid.

[164] Wilson et al., "A Review of Agroterrorism, Biological Crimes, and Biological Warfare Targeting Animal Agriculture."

[165] Goldblatt, personal communication.

[166] Ibid.

[167] Murch, personal communication.

[168] General Accounting Office, "Combating Terrorism: Need for Comprehensive Threat and Risk Assessment of Chemical and Biological Attacks"; General Accounting Office, "Observations on the Threat of Chemical and Biological Terrorism."

[169] Goldblatt, personal communication.

[170] Murch, personal communication.

[171] Horn, statement before the United States Senate Emerging Threats and Capabilities Subcommittee of the Armed Services Committee; Norm Steele, personal communication, March 22, May 24, 2000.

References

Abelson, Philip H. "Biological Warfare." *Science* 286, no. 5445 (November 26, 1999): 1677.

Abrutyn, Elias. "Communicating Infectious Disease Information to the Public." *Emerging Infectious Diseases* 4, no. 3 (July-September 1998). Available online at <http://www.cdc.gov/ncidod/EID/vol4no3/abrutyn.htm>.

Adams, James. "Big Problem—Bad Solution: The Crisis in Critical Infrastructure and the Federal Solution." *Online News Summit '98*, May 18, 1998. Available online at <http://www.terrorism.com/homeland/JamesAdamsUPI speech.htm>.

Advisory Panel to Assess Domestic Response Capabilities for Terrorism Involving Weapons of Mass Destruction. "First Annual Report to the President and the Congress, Part I: Assessing the Threat." December 15, 1999.

"Agriculture Fears Terrorist Threats to Food Supply." *Department of Energy and Nuclear Regulatory Commission Monthly Terrorism and Security Report* 3, no. 10 (October 1999).

Alexander, L. "Decontaminating Civilian Facilities: Biological Agents and Toxins." Institute for Defense Analyses, report no. IDA–P–3365.

Alliance for America. "Bombings of Two USDA Facilities in Washington State." Memorandum, July 7, 1998.

———. "Congress Holds Hearings on Eco-Terror." July 7, 1998.

Alper, Joseph. "From the Bioweapons Trenches, New Tools for Battling Microbes." *Science* 284, no. 5421 (June 11, 1999): 1754–1755.

American Crop Protection Association. "About ACPA." Available online at <http://www.acpa.org>.

American Dairy Science Association. "American Dairy Science Association." Available online at <http://www.adsa.org>.

American Phytopathological Society. "Plant Pathologists To Discuss Anti-Crop Bioterrorism and Food Security, August 1999." *PR Newswire* (July 21, 1999).

———. World Wide Web Resources for Reporting, Understanding, and Evaluating Plant Diseases. 1999.

American Poultry Association. "American Poultry Association." Available online at <http://www.ampltya.com>.

American Society of Animal Science. "American Society of Animal Science." Available online at <http://www.asas.org>.

American Society for Microbiology. "Public Policy: FY 2000 Appropriation for the United States Department of Agriculture and Food and Drug Administration." Available online at <http://asmusa.org/pasrc/usdafdafy2000.htm>.

Anbarasan, Ethirajan. "Genetic Weapons: A 21st Century Nightmare?" *The UNESCO Courier* 52, no. 3 (1999): 37–39.

Anthony, C. "Review of *The Eleventh Plague: The Politics of Biological and Chemical Warfare* by Leonard Cole." *Science News* 153, no. 25 (June 20, 1998): 386.

"Anthrax! Scary, Costly, Real." *Security* 36, no. 2 (1999): 7–9.

APIC Bioterrorism Task Force and CDC Hospital Infections Program Bioterrorism Working Group. "Bioterrorism Readiness Plan: A Template for Healthcare Facilities." April 13, 1999.

Associated Press. "Animal Disease Lab Tries To Ease Neighbors' Fears." *The Washington Post*, November 21, 1999, A32–33.

Atkinson, David. "Air Force Takes Incremental Approach to Chem-Bio Defense." *Defense Daily* 200, no. 48 (October 20, 1998): 1.

Atlas, Ronald M. "Combating the Threat of Biowarfare and Bioterrorism." *Bioscience* 49, no. 6 (June 1999): 465–477.

———. "The Medical Threat of Biological Weapons." *Critical Reviews in Microbiology* 24, no. 3 (1998): 157–168.

———, and Richard E. Weller. "Academe and the Threat of Biological Terrorism." *The Chronicle of Higher Education* 45, no. 49 (August 13, 1999): B6.

Bartlett, John G. "Applying Lessons Learned from Anthrax Case History to Other Scenarios." *Emerging Infectious Diseases* 5, no. 4 (July/August 1999). Available online at <http://www.cdc.gov/nciod/EID/vol5no4/bartlett.htm>.

Bender, Bryan. "DARPA Seeks Radical Bacteria Detectors." *Jane's Defense Weekly* (August 26, 1998): 1.

Bettag, Tom, Ted Koppel, and Leroy Sievers. "More Dangerous Fictions." *The Washington Post*, November 13, 1999, A27.

"Bioterrorism, Foodborne Diseases, and 'Superbugs' Pose New Threats to U.S. Cities." *PR Newswire* (October 6, 1998).

"Bioterrorism May Be Threat to Crops." *USA Today* 128, no. 2655 (1999): 7.

"Bioterrorism Safeguards Raise Questions About Future Research." *HazMat Transport News* 19, no. 6 (June 1, 1998).

Bodamer, David. "From Biological Weapons to Biological Breakthroughs." *Civil Engineering* 68, no. 10 (October 1998): 58.

"Briefs." *Food Chemical News* 41, no. 9 (April 19, 1999).

Butler, Declan. "Talks Start on Policing Bio-Weapons Ban." *Nature* 388, no. 6640 (July 24, 1997): 317.

Canadian Broadcasting Corporation. "Biological Warfare and the Soviet Union." Available online at <http://www.tv.cbc.ca/national/pgminfo/redlies/index.html>.

Carter, Ashton J., John M. Deutch, and Philip D. Zelikow. "Catastrophic Terrorism." *Foreign Affairs* 77, no. 6 (November/December 1998): 80–94.

Carus, W. Seth. "Biohazard: Assessing the Bioterrorism Threat." *The New Republic* 221 (August 2, 1999): 14–16.

———. "Biological Warfare Threats in Perspective." *Critical Reviews in Microbiology* 24 (1998): 149–155.

———. "Bioterrorism and Biocrimes: The Illicit Use of Biological Agents in the 20ᵗʰ Century." Center for Counterproliferation Research, National Defense University (August 1998; July 1999 revision).

———. Testimony before a joint hearing of the Senate Select Committee on Intelligence and the Senate Judiciary Committee Subcommittee on Technology, Terrorism, and Government Information, Washington, DC (March 4, 1998).

———. "The Threat of Bioterrorism." *Strategic Forum* no. 127, Institute for National Strategic Studies, National Defense University Press (September 1997).

Castelli, Christopher J. "Commission's First Report Says Americans Are Becoming Increasingly Vulnerable." *Inside the Pentagon,* September 14, 1999.

Centers for Disease Control and Prevention. "Bioterrorism Alleging Use of Anthrax and Interim Guidelines for Management—United States, 1998." *JAMA* 281, no. 9 (March 3, 1999): 787–789.

———. "CDC Performance Plans. IV: Infectious Diseases." Available online at <http://www.cdc.gov/od/perfpln/2000iv.htm>.

———. "CDC Performance Plans. XIV: Public Health Response to Terrorism." Available online at <http://www.cdc.gov/od/perfpln/2000xiv.htm>.

———, Division of Laboratory Studies. "Response to Bioterrorism: The Role of the Clinical Laboratory: Program Description." Available online at <http://www.phppo.cdc.gov/dls/nltn/btca.asp>.

Center for Nonproliferation Studies. "Federal Funding to Combat Terrorism." Available online at <http://www.cns.miis.edu/research/cbw/terfund.htm>.

Chalk, Peter. Unpublished review of agricultural bioterrorism. The RAND Corporation.

Charatan, Fred. "Biohazard." *British Medical Journal* 319, no. 7216 (October 16, 1999): 1077.

Choo, Kristin. "A Plague in the Making." *ABA Journal* 85 (December 1999): 18–20.

Chown, Marcus. "A Slight Nuclear Chill Could Destroy the World's Crops." *New Scientist* 108 (1985): 18.

Christopher, George W. et al. "Biological Warfare: A Historical Perspective." *JAMA* 278, no. 5 (August 6, 1997): 412–417.

"CIA Says Rogue-State Missile Threat Is Rising." *The Wall Street Journal,* September 10, 1999, A20.

Clarke, Richard A. "Finding the Right Balance Against Bioterrorism." *Emerging Infectious Diseases* 5, no. 4 (July/August 1999). Available online at <http://www.cdc.gov/ncidod/EID/vol5no4/clarke.htm>.

Clinton, William J. "Remarks at the National Academy of Sciences, January 22, 1999." *Weekly Compilation of Presidential Documents* 35 (3): 103–106.

Cobbold, Richard. "Defending Against the Threat from Biological and Chemical Weapons." *RUSI Journal* 144, no. 5 (October 1999): 87–88.

Cohen, Eliot A. "Review of Biotechnology, Weapons, and Humanity by the British Medical Association." *Foreign Affairs* 78, no. 4 (July/August 1999): 133.

Cohen, Hillel W., Robert M. Gould, and Victor W. Sidel. "Bioterrorism Initiatives: Public Health in Reverse?" *American Journal of Public Health* 89, no. 11 (November 1999): 1629–1631.

Cohen, Linda R., and Roger G. Noll. "The Future of National Laboratories." *Proceedings of the Academy of Natural Sciences* 93 (November 1996): 12678–12685.

Cohen, Philip. "A Terrifying Power." *New Scientist* 161, no. 2171 (January 30, 1999): 10

Cohen, William S. "Preparing for a Grave New World." *The Washington Post,* July 26, 1999, A19.

Cole, Leonard A. "A Plague of Publicity." *The Washington Post,* August 16, 1999, A15.

———. "The Specter of Biological Weapons." *Scientific American* 275, no. 6 (December 1996): 60–65.

Coleman, Gary. "Challenges Enough for a Century." *Journal of Environmental Health* 62, no. 1(July/August 1999): 4–7.

Commission to Assess the Organization of the Federal Government to Combat the Proliferation of Weapons of Mass Destruction. "Combating Proliferation of Weapons of Mass Destruction." Report to the United States Senate, July 14, 1999.

Council for Agricultural Science and Technology. "Animal Agriculture and Global Food Supply." Task Force Report No. 135 (1999).

Couzin, Jennifer. "Preparing to Counter an Invisible Adversary." *U.S. News and World Report* 126, no. 7 (February 22, 1999): 61.

Cragin, Charles L., Dolores M. Etter, John Doesburg, and Raymond Dominguez. Statement before the Military Research and Development Subcommittee of the House Armed Services Committee regarding Department of Defense efforts to support domestic emergency preparedness for responding to incidents involving weapons of mass destruction, March 11, 1999. Available online at <http://www.nbcindustrygroup.com/document1.htm>.

Crane, J.T. "Hot Zone Laboratories." *ASHRAE Journal* 41, no. 6 (1999): 28–31.

Critical Infrastructure Assurance Office. "National Plan for Information Systems Protection." January 2000. Available online at <http://www.ciao.ncr.gov/ CIAO_Document_Library/document_index_date.htm>.

Damsteegt, Vern D. "New and Emerging Plant Viruses." APSnet (August 1–September 15, 1999). Available online at <http://www. apsnet.org/online/feature/NewViruses/top.html>.

Danzig, Richard, and Pamela B. Berkowsky. "Why Should We Be Concerned About Biological Warfare?" *JAMA* 278, no. 5 (August 6, 1999): 431–432.

Davis, Christopher J. "Nuclear Blindness: An Overview of the Biological Weapons Programs of the Former Soviet Union and Iraq." *Emerging Infectious Diseases* 5, no. 4 (July/August 1999). Available online at <http://www.cdc.gov/ ncidod/EID/vol5no4/davis.htm>.

Deen, Wallace A. Abstract of "A Historical Perspective of Bioterrorism and Its Implications for North American Agriculture." APSnet, Abstracts of the 1999 American Phytopathological Society Annual Meeting Symposium: Plant Pathology's Role in Anti-Crop Bioterrorism and Food Security (September 15–October 31, 1999). Available online at <http://www. apsnet.org/online/feature/biosecurity/abstract.htm>.

Defense Intelligence Agency. "The Worldwide Agricultural Biological Warfare Threat." Unclassified briefing, Biological Warfare Assessments Division, Office for Counterproliferation Support, 2000.

"Defense Watch: The Latest Word on Trends and Developments in Defense and Aerospace." *Defense Daily* 200, no. 46 (1998): 1.

"Designed for Danger." *Design News* 55, no. 2 (January 17, 2000): 28.

Dickinson, James G. "Security of FGDA Bioterrorism Research Probed." *Medical Marketing and Media* 34, no. 9 (September 1999): 38.

Dobbs, M. "An Obscure Chief in U.S. War on Terror." *The Washington Post,* April 2, 2000, A1.

Dornheim, Michael A. "Virtual Warfare." *Aviation Week and Space Technology* 151, no. 14 (October 4, 1999): 19.

Drake, Jessica K. "After All These Years: Chem-Bio Defense Unequal to Threat." *National Defense* 83, no. 543 (December 1998): 39.

"A Dramatic Development in Biotechnology?" *Genetic Engineer and Biotechnologist* 11 (6): 6

Elvin, John. "Bioterrorism Breeds a Growth Industry." *Insight on the News* 15, no. 45 (December 6, 1999): 35.

Embassy of the Russian Federation. "Russia Denies Allegations of Violating Biological Weapons Ban." Press release no. 15, April 1, 1998.

Ember, Lois R. "Bioterrorism: Countering the Threat." *Chemical and Engineering News* 77, no. 27 (July 5, 1999): 8–17.

————. "Countering the Spread of Chemical and Biological Weapons." *Chemical and Engineering News* 77, no. 22 (May 31, 1999): 7.

————. "DARPA Expands R&D on Biowarfare Defense Tools." *Chemical and Engineering News* 76, no. 7 (February 16, 1998): 7.

————. "A Double-Edged Sword." *Chemical and Engineering News* 77, no. 49 (December 6, 1999): 109–117.

Emergency Response and Research Institute. "Counter-Terrorism Archive." Available online at <http://www.emergency.com/cntrterr.htm>.

Enders, Walter, and Todd Sandler. "Transnational Terrorism in the Post-Cold War Era." Iowa State University, Department of Economics staff paper 309 (April 1998).

Environmental Protection Agency. "Counter-Terrorism." Available online at <http://www.epa.gov/swercepp/cntr-ter.html>. April 7, 1999, update.

Erwin, Sandra I. "Chemical, Biological Defense Program Runs 'Hot & Cold.'" *National Defense* 84, no. 550 (September 1999): 31–32.

————. "Commanders Told To Report False Alarms." *National Defense* 84, no. 550 (September 1999): 33–34.

————. "U.S. Deployments Derailed by Threat of Mass Terror?" *National Defense* 84, no. 550 (September 1999): 34.

Fabian, Nelson. "Bioterrorism and Our Professional Image." *Journal of Environmental Health* 61, no. 7 (March 1999): 61–62.

Falkenrath, Richard A. "Unknowable Threats, Prudent Policies." *Survival* 40, no. 4 (Winter 1998–1999): 179–183.

Federal Bureau of Investigation. "Awareness of National Security Issues and Response (ANSIR) Program." Updated April 6, 1998. Available online at <http://www.fbi.gov/programs/ansir/ansir.htm>.

Federal Emergency Management Agency. "Backgrounder: Terrorism." Available online at <http://www.fema.gov/library/terror.htm>.

————. "Federal Response Plan." Executive Overview, April 1999.

————. "Rapid Response Information System." Available online at <http://www.fema.gov/rris>.

————. "Response and Recovery: Federal Response Plan." Available online at <http://www.fema.gov/r-n-r/frp>.

Federation of American Scientists, Working Group on Biological Weapons Verification. Report of the Subgroup on Investigation of Alleged Release of Biological or Toxin Weapons Agents (April 1996).

Federation of Animal Science Societies. "About FASS." Available online at <http://www.fass.org>.

Federov, Lev. "It Might Well Be a BW Virus." *Moscow News* 27 (July 1999): 3.

Fehr, Stephen C. "Worries About Public Disclosure, Threat of Terrorism." *The Washington Post*, October 10, 1999.

Fishman, Rachelle H.B. "Scientists Propose Means to Peace and Safety." *The Lancet* 352, no. 9141 (November 21, 1998): 1685.

Fitzgerald, Clare. "Anti-Terrorism Software Models Real Effects of Biological Weapons." *Security* 36, no. 7 (July 1999): 9–10

Foer, Franklin. "Toxic Shock." *The New Republic* 218, no. 11 (March 16, 1998): 12–15.

Foote, Sheila. "U.S. Should Do More To Prevent Proliferation, Cochran Says." *Defense Daily* 198, no. 8 (January 13, 1998): 1.

Forster, Robert L. "Ground Surveillance." APSnet, Abstracts of the 1999 American Phytopathological Society Annual Meeting Symposium: Plant Pathology's Role in Anti-Crop Bioterrorism and Food Security (September 15–October 31, 1999). Available online at <http://www.apsnet.org/online/feature/BioSecurity/Top.html>.

Frankel, David H. "U.S. Experts Take the Threat of Bioterrorism Seriously." *The Lancet* 353, no. 9154 (February 27, 1999): 734.

Franz, David R. Posture statement for the Joint Committee on Judiciary and Intelligence, United States Senate, Second Session, 105th Congress. "International Biological Warfare Threat in the Continental United States." March 4, 1998.

———, et al. "Clinical Recognition and Management of Patients Exposed to Biological Warfare Agents." *JAMA* 278, no. 5 (August 6, 1999): 399–411.

Frazier, Tom W. "Bioterrorism and Agriculture." APSnet, Abstracts of the 1999 Annual American Phytopathological Society Meeting Symposium: Plant Pathology's Role in Anti-Crop Bioterrorism and Food Security (September 15–October 31, 1999). Available online at <http://www.apsnet.org/online/feature/BioSecurity/Top.html>.

Freedberg, Sidney J., Marilyn W. Serafini, and Siobhan Gorman. "Be Afraid, Be Moderately Afraid." *National Journal* 31, no. 13 (March 27, 1999): 806–817.

"Fruit Producers Demand Solution to Poisoned Grapes Issue." *Santiago El Mercurio*, August 29, 1999.

Gale Group. "2000 Budget Proposal for FDA." Gale Group Newsletter DB, February 2, 1999.

Garrett, Laurie. *The Coming Plague: Newly Emerging Diseases in a World Out of Balance.* New York: Farrar Straus Giroux, 1994.

———. "Delayed Russian Anthrax Shipment Concerns U.S." Seattletimes.com, Nation and World. Available online at <http://www.seattletimes.com/news/nation-world/html98/altgerm_021998.html>.

General Accounting Office. "Chemical and Biological Defense: Coordination of Nonmedical Chemical and Biological R&D Programs." Letter Report, August 16, 1999, GAO/NSIAD–99–160. Available online at <http://frwebgate. access.gpo.gov>.

——— . "Combating Terrorism: Analysis of Potential Emergency Response Equipment and Sustainment Costs." Letter Report, June 9, 1999, GAO/NSIAD–99–151. Available online at <http://frwebgate.access. gpo.gov>.

——— . "Combating Terrorism: Chemical and Biological Medical Supplies are Poorly Managed." Letter Report, October 29, 1999, GAO/HEHS/ AIMD–00–36. Abstract available online at http://frwebgate4. access.gpo.gov.

——— . "Combating Terrorism: FBI's Use of Federal Funds for Counterterrorism-Related Activities (Fiscal Years 1995–1998)." Letter Report, November 20, 1998, GAO/GGD–99–7. Available online at <http://frwebgate.access. gpo.gov>.

——— . "Combating Terrorism: Issues to be Resolved to Improve Counterterrorism Operations." Letter Report, May 13, 1999, GAO/NSIAD–99–135. Available online at <http://frwebgate4.access.gpo.gov>.

——— . "Combating Terrorism: Need for Comprehensive Threat and Risk Assessments of Chemical and Biological Attacks." Letter Report, September 7, 1999, GAO/NSIAD–99–163. Available online at <http://frwebgate.access. gpo.gov>.

——— . "Combating Terrorism: Observations on Biological Terrorism and Public Health Initiatives." Testimony, March 16, 1999, GAO/T–NSIAD–99–112. Available online at <http://frwebgate.access.gpo.gov>.

——— . "Combating Terrorism: Observations on Crosscutting Issues." Testimony, April 23, 1998, GAO/T–NSIAD–98–164. Available online at <http://frwebgate.access.gpo.gov>.

——— . "Combating Terrorism: Observations on the Growth of Federal Programs." Testimony, June 9, 1999, GAO/T–NSIAD–99–181. Available online at <http://frwebgate.access.gpo.gov>.

——— . "Combating Terrorism: Observations on the Nunn-Lugar-Domenici Domestic Preparedness Program." Testimony, October 2, 1998, GAO/T– NSIAD–99–16. Available online at <http://frwebgate.access.gpo.gov>.

——— . "Combating Terrorism: Opportunities to Improve Domestic Preparedness Program Focus and Efficiency." Letter Report, November 12, 1998, GAO/NSIAD–99–3. Abstract available online at <http://frwebgate4.access. gpo.gov>.

——— . "Combating Terrorism: Selected Challenges and Related Recommendations." Report, September 20, 2001, GAO/NSIAD–01–822. Available online at <http://www.gao.gov>.

——— . "Combating Terrorism: Threat and Risk Assessments Can Help Prioritize and Target Program Investments." Letter Report, April 9, 1998, GAO/ NSIAD–98–74. Abstract available online at <http://frwebgate4.access. gpo.gov>.

——— . "Combating Terrorism: Use of National Guard Teams is Unclear." Testimony, June 23, 1999, GAO/T–NSIAD–99–185. Available online at <http://frwebgate.access.gpo.gov>.

——— . "Food Safety: Agencies Should Further Test Plans for Responding to Deliberate Contamination." Letter Report, October 27, 1999, GAO/RCED–00–3. Available online at <http://frwebgate.access.gpo.gov>.

——— . "Observations on Federal Spending to Combat Terrorism." Testimony, March 11, 1999, GAO/T–NSIAD/GGD–99–107. Available online at <http://frwebgate.access.gpo.gov>.

——— . "Observations on the Threat of Chemical and Biological Terrorism." Testimony, October 20, 1999, GAO/T–NSIAD–00–50. Available online at <http://frwebgate.access.gpo.gov>.

——— . "U.S. Agriculture: Status of the Farm Sector." Fact Sheet for Congressional Committees. GAO/RCED–95–104FS, March 1995.

"Genetics Activists Create Superweed Kit." Cultural Terrorist Agency, January 24, 1999.

George, Kerry A. "Biological Warfare: The Threat of the Millennium." *United States Naval Institute Proceedings* 125, no. 7 (July 1999): 86–87.

Gips, Michael. "Bioterrorism in Our Midst?" *Security Management* 41, no. 11 (November 1997): 12.

Goldberg, Paul. "Killer Bacteria. Review of *Anthrax: The Investigation of a Deadly Outbreak* by Jeanne Guillemin." *New York Times Book Review,* December 19, 1999: 27.

Goldblatt, Michael. Personal communication, April 6, 2000.

Goldstein, Steve. "U.S. Could Face New Terror Tactic: Agricultural Warfare." *The Philadelphia Inquirer,* June 22, 1999.

Gonzalez, Miley. Statement of Dr. I. Miley Gonzalez, Under Secretary of Agriculture for Research, Education, and Economics, before the Subcommittee on Agriculture, Rural Development, and Related Agencies of the Senate Committee on Appropriations. Available online at <http://www.reeusda.gov/ legis/img_sen.htm>.

Gorman, Siobhan. "Bioterror Down on the Farm." *National Journal* 31, no.13 (March 27, 1999): 812–813.

——— . "Future Pharmers of America." *National Journal* 31, no. 6 (February 6, 1999): 355–356.

Gosden, Christine M. Testimony before the Senate Judiciary Subcommittee on Technology, Terrorism, and Government and the Senate Select Committee on Intelligence on Chemical and Biological Weapons Threats to America: Are We Prepared? April 22, 1998.

Greenberg, Daniel S. "The Bioterrorism Panic." *The Washington Post,* March 16, 1999.

Grinter, Lawrence E., and Barry R. Schneider, eds. *Battlefield of the Future: 21ˢᵗ Century Warfare Issues.* Maxwell Air Force Base, AL: Air University Press, 1995.

Gromer, Cliff, and Jim Wilson. "Weapons of Mass Destruction." *Popular Mechanics* 175, no. 6 (June 1998): 80–85.

Grosscup, Beau. "The New Terrorism: Fanaticism and the Arms of Mass Destruction." *Choice* 37, no. 5 (January 2000): 1011.

Gunby, Phil. "Physicians Face Bioterrorism." *JAMA* 281, no. 13 (April 7, 1999): 1162.

Guterman, Lila. "Death in the Air." *New Scientist* 159, no. 2151 (September 12, 1998): 11.

Halbfinger, David M. "Residents Near Lab Taking Germ Plan Matter-of-Factly." *The New York Times,* September 23, 1999, B6.

Hall, Gene L., and Joe Fields. "Farm Bureau Wins Bid to Protect Confidentiality." American Farm Bureau Federation News Releases, February 10, 2000. Available online at <http://www.fb.org/news/nr/nr2000/nr0210.html>.

Hall, Stephen S. "Science-Fiction Policy." *Technology Review* 101, no. 6 (November/December 1998): 92–93.

Halsey, Eugenia. "Food Terrorism a Possibility, Report Warns." CNN Interactive, August 5, 1997. Accessed online at <http://www.cnn.com>.

Hamburg, Margaret A. "Addressing Bioterrorist Threats: Where Do We Go From Here?" *Emerging Infectious Diseases* 5, no. 4 (July/August 1999). Available online at <http://www.cdc.gov/ncidod/EID/vol5no4/hamburg.htm>.

Handbook for Interagency Management of Complex Contingency Operations. Selected pages attached to White House, 1997 PDD–56.

Haskell, Bob. "Guard WMD Teams Have Fan in Virginia Governor." *National Guard* 53, no. 9 (September 1999): 74–75.

Henderson, Donald A. "About the First National Symposium on Medical and Health Response to Bioterrorism." *Emerging Infectious Diseases* 5, no. 4 (July/August 1999). Available online at <http://www.cdc.gov/ncidod/EID/vol5no4/dahendrsn.htm>.

——— . "The Looming Threat of Bioterrorism." *Science* 283, no. 5406 (February 26, 1999): 1279–1282.

——— . "Weapons for the Future." *The Lancet* 354 (Supplement, December 1999): S64.

Henry L. Stimson Center. *CBW Chronicle* 2, no. 2 (September 1996).

———. "Concerns Renewed About Russia's Bio Weapons Program." *CBW Chronicle* 2, no. 4 (May 1998).

Hersman, Rebecca, and W. Seth Carus. "DOD and Consequence Management: Mitigating the Effects of Chemical and Biological Attack." *Strategic Forum* no. 169, Institute for National Strategic Studies, National Defense University (December 1999).

Heylin, Michael. "Ag Biotech's Promise Clouded by Consumer Fear." *Chemical and Engineering News* 77, no. 49 (December 6, 1999): 73–88.

———. "Biological Weapons: A View of the Reality. Review of *The Biology of Doom* by Ed Regis." *Chemical and Engineering News* 78, no. 10 (March 6, 2000): 65–66.

———. "Bioterrorism: Very Tough Choices." *Chemical and Engineering News* 77, no. 32 (August 9, 1999): 26.

Hicks and Associates, Inc. "Homeland Defense: Threats and Policies in Transition." July 15, 1998. Available online at <http://www.terrorism.com/homeland/CT&CIAfinal.html>.

Hickson, R. "Subtle Forms of Strategic Indirect Warfare: Infecting 'Soft' Biological Targets; Some Psychological, Economic, and Cultural Consequences." AP-Snet, Abstracts of the 1999 Annual American Phytopathological Society Meeting Symposium: Plant Pathology's Role in Anti-Crop Bioterrorism and Food Security (September 15–October 31, 1999). Available online at <http://www.apsnet.org/online/feature/BioSecurity/ Top.html>.

Hoffman, Bruce. "Terrorism with Biological and Chemical Weapons: Calibrating Risks and Responses." *Survival* 40, no. 2 (Summer 1998): 185.

Holloway, Harry C., et al., "The Threat of Biological Weapons: Prophylaxis and Mitigation of Psychological and Social Consequences." *JAMA* 278, no. 5 (August 6, 1997): 425–427.

Horn, Floyd P. Statement before the United States Senate Emerging Threats and Capabilities Subcommittee of the Armed Services Committee, October 27, 1999. Available online at <http://www.senate.gov/~armed_services/hearings/1999/e991027.htm>.

———. Personal communication, May 2, 2000.

Hughes, James M. "The Emerging Threat of Bioterrorism." *Emerging Infectious Diseases* 5, no. 4 (July/August 1999). Available online at <http://www.cdc.gov/ncidod/EID/vol5no4/hughes.htm>.

———. Statement before the Subcommittee on Technology, Terrorism, and Government Information, Subcommittee on Youth Violence, Committee on the Judiciary, U.S. Senate, April 20, 1999. Available online at <http://www.bt.cdc.gov/press/Hughes_04201999.asp>.

Hulse, Carl. "Group Puts Disaster Data on Internet." *The New York Times,* September 12, 1999, 32.

————. "Readying Emergency Teams for Terrorist Attacks." *The New York Times,* July 3, 1999, 9.

Hurlbert, Ronald E. "Microbiology 101 Internet Text: Chapter XV, Addendum: Biological Weapons; Malignant Biology." Accessed at <http://www.wsu.edu/~hurlburt/pages/101biologicalweapons.html>.

Huxsoll, David L. "Biological Terrorism: Identifying and Protecting Our Infrastructure." APSnet, Abstracts of the 1999 American Phytopathological Society Annual Meeting Symposium: Plant Pathology's Role in Anti-Crop Bioterrorism and Food Security (September 15–October 31, 1999). Available online at <http://www.apsnet.org/online/feature/BioSecurity/Top.html>.

Jackson, Richard. Statement before the Subcommittee on Labor, Health and Human Services, and Education, Committee on Appropriations, U.S. Senate, June 2, 1998. Available online at <http://www.bt.cdc.gov/press/Jackson_1.asp>.

Jacobs, Madeleine. "Monsters Under the Bed?" *Chemical Engineering News* 77, no. 27 (July 5, 1999): 3.

Johnson, James A. "Interview with Brigadier General Donna F. Barbisch, D.H.A., Senior Advisor to the Biological Warfare Improved Response Program." *Journal of Healthcare Management* 44, no. 5 (September/October 1999): 329–334.

Johnson, Peter. "'Nightline' Simulates Battle Plans for 'Biowar.'" *USA Today,* September 28, 1999, 3D.

Joint Bradford Project on Strengthening of the Biological and Toxic Weapons Convention and Preventing Biological Warfare—Stockholm International Peace Research Institute. "Chemical and Biological Warfare Project." 1999. Accessed online at <http://www.brad.ac.uk/acad/sbtwc>.

"Joint Statement on a Protocol to the Convention on the Prohibition of Biological Weapons." *Weekly Compilation of Presidential Documents* 34, no. 36 (September 7, 1998): 1693–1694.

Jurenas, Remy. "Economic Sanctions and U.S. Agricultural Exports." Congressional Research Service Issue Brief for Congress, March 11, 1999.

Kaiser, Jocelyn. "Agricultural Research: Report Tells USDA to Narrow Its Focus." *Science* 285, no. 5425 (July 9, 1999): 181.

Kamp, Karl-Heinz. "Nuclear Terrorism Is Not the Core Problem." *Survival* 40, no. 4 (Winter 1998–1999): 168–171.

Kaufmann, Arnold F., Martin I. Meltzer, and George P. Schmid. "The Economic Impact of a Bioterrorist Attack: Are Prevention and Postattack Intervention Programs Justifiable?" *Emerging Infectious Diseases* 3, no. 2 (April–June 1997). Available online at <http://www.cdc.gov/ncidod/EID/vol3no2/kaufman.htm>.

Kemp, Damian. "Hunting To Engineer UK Biological-Detection Systems." *Jane's Defense Weekly* 31, no. 11 (March 17, 1999): 1.

Keppel, David. "When Fears of Bioterrorism Grow." *The New York Times,* October 21, 1999, A24.

Kiernan, Vincent. "Confronting the Threat of Bioterrorism." *The Chronicle of Higher Education* 45, no. 25 (February 26, 1999): A18–22.

Komarow, Steven. "Military Chiefs Set Up Command To Address U.S. Terrorist Threats." *USA Today,* October 8, 1999, 6A.

Kortepeter, Mark G., and Gerald W. Parker. "Potential Biological Weapons Threats." *Emerging Infectious Diseases* 5, no. 4 (July/August 1999). Available online at <http://www.cdc.gov/ncidod/EID/vol5no4/kortepeter.htm>.

Kovarovic, P.C. "Will the U.S. Eventually Be Held Hostage by Its High-Technology Conventional Weapons? The Effect Technology Transfer Has on International Terrorism." Proceedings of the Technology Transfer Society Annual Symposium and Exhibit (1990).

Landersman, Stuart D. "The New Face of War: Weapons of Mass Destruction and the Revitalization of America's Transoceanic Military Strategy." *United States Naval Institute Proceedings* 125, no. 11 (November 1999): 82.

Lawler, Andrew. "Senate Calls for Pathogen Alert." *Science* 271, no. 1485 (March 15, 1996).

Leach, Jan E. "Assuring Food Security: Detecting and Controlling Modified Pathogens." APSnet, Abstracts of the 1999 American Phytopathological Society Annual Meeting Symposium: Plant Pathology's Role in Anti-Crop Bioterrorism and Food Security (September 15–October 31, 1999). Available online at <http://www.apsnet.org/online/feature/BioSecurity/Top.html>.

Lederberg, Joshua. "Infectious Disease and Biological Weapons." *JAMA* 278, no. 5 (August 6, 1997): 435–436.

Leitenberg, Milton. "Biological Weapons: A Reawakened Concern." *The World & I* 14, no. 1 (January 1999): 289–305.

Lewis, Eugene. "Review of *The Ultimate Terrorists* by Jessica Stern." *Choice* 36 (July 1999): 2015.

Lillibridge, Scott. Statement before the Subcommittee on National Security, Veterans Affairs, and International Relations, Committee on Government Reform, U.S. House of Representatives, September 22, 1999. Available online at <http://www.bt.cdc.gov/press/Lill_09221999.asp>.

Loeb, Vernon. "Anthrax Vial Smuggled In To Make A Point at Hill Hearing." *The Washington Post,* March 4, 1999, A11.

Louisiana Cooperative Extension Services. "Welcome to EDEN: Extension Disaster Education Network." Available online at <http://www.agctr.lso.edu/eden>.

MacKenzie, Debora. "Run, Radish, Run." *New Scientist* 164, no. 2217 (December 18, 1999): 36–39.

Maddaloni, Chris. "Homeland Defense." *National Guard* 54, no. 1 (January 2000): 24–25.

Madden, Laurence V., and Harold Scherm. "Epidemiology and Risk Prediction." APSnet, Abstracts of the 1999 American Phytopathological Society Annual Meeting Symposium: Plant Pathology's Role in Anti-Crop Bioterrorism and Food Security (September 15–October 31, 1999). Available online at <http://www.apsnet.org/online/feature/BioSecurity/Top.html>.

"Man Who Poisoned Food Gets 11-Year Jail Term." *The Boston Globe*, September 24, 1999, A16.

Mangold, Tom, and Jeff Goldberg. *Plague Wars: The Terrifying Reality of Biological Warfare*. New York: St. Martin's Press, 2000.

Manning, Anita. "U.S. 'Not Ready' for Biological Threats. Officials Say a Large-Scale Attack Would Overwhelm Response Efforts." *USA Today*, March 11, 1998, 3A.

Marshall, Eliot. "Bioterror Defense Initiative Injects Shot of Cash." *Science* 283 (February 26, 1999): 1234–1235.

——— . "Defending Against Bugs and Bytes." *Science* 283 (January 29, 1999): 612–613.

Marwick, Charles. "Scary Scenarios Spark Action at Bioterrorism Symposium." *JAMA* 281, no. 12 (March 1999): 1071–1073.

McCann, S. Anthony. "View From the Hill: Congressional Efforts To Address Bioterrorism." *Emerging Infectious Diseases* 5, no. 4 (July/August 1999). Available online at <http://www.cdc.gov/ncidod/EID/vol5no4/mccann.htm>.

McCarthy, Michael. "USA Plans Major Effort To Counter Biowarfare." *The Lancet* 351, no. 9116 (May 30, 1998): 1641.

McCutcheon, Chuck. "Citizen-Soldiers Take on a Formidable New Mission." *CQ Weekly* 57, no. 10 (March 6, 1999): 524–525.

McDade, Joseph E. "Addressing the Potential Threat of Bioterrorism—Value Added to an Improved Public Health Infrastructure." *Emerging Infectious Diseases* 5, no. 4 (July/August 1999). Available online at <http://www.cdc.gov/ncidod/EID/vol5no4/mcdade.htm>.

Mifflin, Laurie. "Biological Timeliness." *The New York Times*, February 25, 1998, 8.

Miller, Judith. "Clinton Seeks Additional $300 Million To Fight Bioterrorism." *The New York Times*, June 9, 1998, A16.

——— . "Killer Germs." *The New York Times* Upfront 132, no. 5 (November 1, 1999): 14–15.

——— . "U.S. To Reduce Bureaucracy in Responding to Terrorism." *The New York Times*, October 8, 1998, 26.

———. "U.S. To Use Lab for More Study of Bioterrorism." *The New York Times,* September 22, 1999, A1, A25.

———. "U.S. Unprepared for Bioterrorism, Experts Say." *The New York Times,* June 3, 1998, A14.

Monath, Thomas P., and Lance K. Gordon. "Strengthening the Biological Weapons Convention." *Science* 282, no. 5393 (November 20, 1998): 1423.

Morgan-Clyborne, Sarah A., Frank J. Cole, and Matthew R. Whipple. "Protection from Chemical and Biological Threats." *Army Logistician* 31, no. 4 (July/August 1999): 13–15.

Morse, S.A. "About the International Conference on Emerging Infectious Diseases." *Emerging Infectious Diseases* 4, no. 3 (1998): 353.

Muradian, Vago. "U.S.–U.K. To Cooperate on Chem-Bio Efforts." *Defense Daily* 199, no. 46 (June 4, 1998): 1.

Murch, Randall. Personal communication, April 17, 2000.

Murphy, Frederick A. "Emerging Zoonoses." *Emerging Infectious Diseases* 4, no. 3 (July–September 1999): 429–435.

Murphy, J. "Pilot Program To Connect Federal, State, Local Labs To Revolutionize Food Sample Testing." *Food Chemical News,* August 30, 1999.

National Animal Interest Alliance. Request for Action by the Senate Judiciary Committee of the Congress of the United States: Animal Experts Representing Livestock Production, Farming, Science, and Pets to Petition U.S. Senate to Focus on Terrorism. Available online at <http://www.naiaonline.org>.

———. "Terrorism Gains Momentum: Animal Rights and Environmental Criminals Use Violence To Achieve Ends." Available online at <http://www.naiaonline.org/body/articles/archives/arterror.htm>.

National Center for Infectious Diseases. "U.S. Army's Elite Medical Team Prepared To Airlift Patients With Potentially Lethal Contagious Infection." Emerging Infectious Diseases Press Release, June 26, 1999. Available online at <http://www.cdc.gov/ncidod/eid/press_r/christopher.htm>.

National Environmental Health Association. "New Toxin Detector Has Applications in Fighting Bioterrorism." *Journal of Environmental Health* 61, no. 6 (January/February 1999): 36.

"National Guard Trains To Meet WMD Threat." *Army* 49, no. 11 (1999): 57.

National Livestock Producers Association. "Who Is National Livestock Producers Association?" Available online at <http://www.nlpa.org/nlpashrt.htm>.

NBC Industry Group. "Department of Defense Establishes a Weapons of Mass Destruction Advisory Panel." Available online at <http://www.nbcindustrygroup.com/wmdadvisory.htm>.

"Neutralizing Chemical and Biological Warfare Agents—A New Approach." *Journal of Environmental Health* 62, no. 1 (1999): 52.

Newberry, Robert J. Statement before the Senate Armed Services Committee, Subcommittee on Emerging Threats, October 27, 1999. Available online at <http://www.senate.gov/~armed_services/hearings/1999/e991027.htm>.

"NGB Report: No One WMD Ready?" *National Guard* 53, no. 10 (1999): 13–14.

Olson, Kyle B. "Aun Shinrikyo: Once and Future Threat?" *Emerging Infectious Diseases* 5, no. 4 (July/August 1999). Available online at <http://www.cdc.gov/ncidod/EID/vol5no4/olson.htm>.

Orenstein, J.B. "Now Fear This." *The Washington Post*, December 26, 1999, B1.

Osterholm, Michael T. "Bioterrorism Defense." *The New York Times*, August 14, 1998.

Ostroff, Stephen M. Testimony before the U.S. Senate Select Committee on Intelligence and Subcommittee on Technology, Terrorism, and Government, Committee on the Judiciary, March 4, 1998.

O'Toole, Tara. "Smallpox: An Attack Scenario." *Emerging Infectious Diseases* 5, no. 4 (July/August 1999). Available online at <http://www.cdc.gov/ncidod/EID/vol5no4/otoole.htm>.

Pavlin, Julie A. "Epidemiology of Bioterrorism." *Emerging Infectious Diseases* 5, no. 4 (July/August 1999). Available online at <http://www.cdc.gov/ncidod/EID/vol5no4/pavlin.htm>.

Pearson, Graham S. "How To Make Microbes Safer." *Nature* 394, no. 6690 (July 16, 1998): 217–218.

Pilat, Joseph F. "Apocalypse Now—or Never?" *Survival* 40, no. 4 (Winter 1998–1999): 171–175.

Pincus, Walter. "U.S. Preparedness Faulted: Weapons of Mass Destruction Concern Panel." *The Washington Post*, July 9, 1999, A2.

Poultry Science Association. "PSA Welcomes You!" Available online at <http://www.psa.uiuc.edu>.

Preston, Richard. "The Bioweaponeers." *The New Yorker* 74, no. 3 (March 9, 1998): 52.

———. "The Demon in the Freezer." *The New Yorker* 75, no. 18 (July 12, 1999): 44–56+.

———. "Taming the Biological Beast." *The New York Times*, April 21, 1998, 21.

———. "West Nile Mystery." *The New Yorker* 75, no. 31 (October 18–25, 1999): 90–108.

Pringle, Peter. "Bioterrorism." *The Nation* 267, no. 15 (November 2, 1998): 11–17.

———. "Bioterrorism Hits Home." *The Nation* 268, no. 16 (November 9, 1998): 28–32.

Pritchard, Kenneth H. "Review of *America's Achilles' Heel: Nuclear, Biological, and Chemical Terrorism and Covert Attack* by Richard A. Falkenrath,

Robert D. Newman, and Bradley A. Thayer." *Military Review* 79, no. 6 (November/December 1999): 92–94.

RAND Corporation. "Countering the New Terrorism." Available online at <http://www.rand.org/publications/MR/MR989/MR989.pdf>.

"Ready for Trouble?" *American Medical News* 42, no. 17 (1999): 18.

Reiss, Tom. "Now Will We Heed the Biological Threat?" *The New York Times,* February 21, 1998, 11.

Reno, Janet. Statement before the United States Senate Committee on Appropriations, Subcommittee on Commerce, Justice, and State, The Judiciary and Related Agencies, February 4, 1999. Available online at <http://www.usdoj.gov/ag/testimony/1999/agappro020499.htm>.

"Reserves Spearhead Military Response to WMD Terrorism." *Army* 48, no. 5 (1998): 63.

Reynolds, Glenn H. "Hyped Bioterrorism." *The Washington Post,* April 24, 1999, A22.

Reynolds, Jason M. "A Scholarly Expert on Biological Warfare." *The Chronicle of Higher Education* 44, no. 26 (March 6, 1998): A10.

Riechmann, Deb. "Russian Lab Develops Anthrax Strain That Might Defeat U.S. Vaccine." The Associated Press, February 14, 1998.

Roberts, Brad. *Terrorism with Chemical and Biological Weapons: Calibrating Risks and Responses.* Alexandria, VA: Chemical and Biological Arms Control Institute, 1997.

———, and Graham S. Pearson. "Bursting the Biological Bubble: How Prepared Are We for Biowar?" *Jane's International Defense Review,* April 1, 1998, 21–28.

Robertson, Grant. "Crop Warfare Combat Plan Urged." *Calgary Herald,* August 21, 1999.

Robinson, C. Paul, Joan B. Woodard, and Samuel G. Varnado. "Critical Infrastructure: Interlinked and Vulnerable." *Issues in Science and Technology* 15, no. 1 (Fall 1998): 61–67.

Rogers, Paul, Simon Whitby, and Malcolm Dando. "Biological Warfare Against Crops." *Scientific American* 280, no. 6 (June 1999): 70–75

Rose, Gideon. "It Could Happen Here." *Foreign Affairs* 78, no. 2 (March/April 1999): 131–137.

Rosen, Peter. "Coping with Bioterrorism." *British Medical Journal* 320, no. 7227 (January 8, 2000): 71–72.

Russell, Philip K. "Vaccines in Civilian Defense Against Bioterrorism." *Emerging Infectious Diseases* 5, no. 4 (July/August 1999). Available online at <http://www.cdc.gov/ncidod/EID/vol5no4/russell.htm>.

Satcher, David. "Meeting the Public Health Needs of the Nation." *The Officer* 76, no. 1 (January/February 2000): 69–70.

"Satellite Broadcast on Biological Warfare and Terrorism." *Morbidity and Mortality Weekly Report* 48, no. 32 (August 20, 1999): 717.

Schaad, Norm W. "What Is an Effective Pathogen?" APSnet, Abstracts of the 1999 American Phytopathological Society Annual Meeting Symposium: Plant Pathology's Role in Anti-Crop Bioterrorism and Food Security (September 15–October 31, 1999). Available online at <http://www.apsnet.org/online/feature/BioSecurity/Top.html>.

———, et al. "Crop Biosecurity." APSnet, Abstracts of the 1999 American Phytopathological Society Annual Meeting Symposium: Plant Pathology's Role in Anti-Crop Bioterrorism and Food Security (September 15–October 31, 1999). Available online at <http://www.apsnet.org/online/feature/BioSecurity/Top.html>.

Schlesinger, Hank, and Frank Vizard. "Detecting Battlefield Toxins." *Popular Science* 253, no. 4 (October 1998): 45.

Schulte, Paul. "Chemical and Biological Weapons: Issues and Alternatives." *Comparative Strategy* 18, no. 4 (October–December 1999): 329–334.

Schweitzer, Glenn E., and Carole C. Dorsch. *Superterrorism: Assassins, Mobsters, and Weapons of Mass Destruction.* New York: Plenum Press, 1998.

Seigle, Greg. "DoD Asks Congress Not To Cut BW Defence Funds." *Jane's Defence Weekly* 32, no. 11 (September 15, 1999): 1.

———. "Reaction Teams Take Up Posts Across USA Against Potential CBW Strikes." *Jane's Defence Weekly* 30, no. 14 (October 7, 1998): 1.

———. "Suitcase Device Detects Bio Agents." *Jane's Defence Weekly* 31, no. 10 (March 10, 1999): 1.

———. "USA Prepares To Treble Number of RAID Teams." *Jane's Defence Weekly* 31, no. 22 (June 2, 1999): 1.

———. "U.S. Efficiency Drive Aims To Minimise NBC Threats." *Jane's Defence Weekly* 30, no. 14 (October 7, 1999): 1.

———. "U.S. Forces Are Poorly Prepared for Chemical and Biological Attacks." *Jane's Defence Weekly* (September 30, 1998).

Shalala, Donna E. "Bioterrorism: Are We Prepared?" *Emerging Infectious Diseases* 5, no. 4 (July/August 1999). Available online at <http://www.cdc.gov/ncidod/EID/vol5no4/shalala.htm>.

Shell, Ellen R. "Could Mad-Cow Disease Happen Here?" *The Atlantic Monthly* 282, no. 3 (September 1998): 92–106.

Siegrist, David W. "Anti-Bio Terrorism Training Need Realistic Simulations." *National Defense* 84, no. 550 (September 1999): 36–37.

————. "The Threat of Biological Attack: Why Concern Now?" *Emerging Infectious Diseases* 5, no. 4 (July/August 1999). Available online at <http://www.cdc.gov/ncidod/EID/vol5no4/siegrist.htm>.

Simon, Jeffrey D. "Biological Terrorism: Preparing To Meet the Threat." *JAMA* 278, no. 5 (July 6, 1997): 428–429.

Smith, G. Davidson. "Single Issue Terrorism." *Canadian Security Intelligence Service,* commentary no. 74 (Winter 1998).

Smithson, Amy. "A Bio Nightmare." *Bulletin of the Atomic Scientists* 55, no. 4 (July/August 1999): 69–71.

Stapleton, Stephanie. "Biothreat." *American Medical News* 42, no. 15 (April 19, 1999): 26–29.

————. "Medicine Takes Lead in Combating Bioterrorism." *American Medical News* 42, no. 27 (July 19, 1999): 28.

Starr, Barbara. "ACTD: A Near-Term Solution." *Jane's Defence Weekly,* April 1, 1998, 6.

————. "Clinton Briefed on Genetic Engineering Threat." *Jane's Defence Weekly,* April 22, 1998, 13.

Steele, Norm. "Econoterrorism: U.S. Agricultural Productivity, Concentration, and Vulnerability to Biological Weapons." Unclassified Defense Intelligence Assessment for the DOD Futures Intelligence Program, January 14, 2000.

————. "Genetic Engineering of Plants for Biological Weapon Production, Storage, and Dissemination." Unclassified Defense Intelligence Assessment for the DOD Futures Intelligence Program, January 14, 2000.

————. Personal communication, March 22, May 24, 2000.

Steinhauer, Jennifer, and Judith Miller. "In New York Outbreak: Glimpse of Gaps in Biological Defenses." *The New York Times,* October 11, 1999, 1.

Stephenson, Joan. "Emerging Infections on Center Stage at First Major International Meeting." *JAMA* 279, no. 14 (April 8, 1998): 1055.

Stern, Jessica. "Apocalypse Never, But the Threat Is Real." *Survival* 40, no. 4 (Winter 1998–1999): 176–179.

————. "A Lethal Weapon We Must Learn To Recognize." *The New York Times,* October 16, 1999, A19.

————. "The Prospect of Domestic Bioterrorism." *Emerging Infectious Diseases* 5, no. 4 (July/August 1999). Available online at <http://www.cdc.gov/ncidod/EID/vol5no4/stern.htm>.

————. "Taking the Terror Out of Bioterrorism." *The New York Times,* April 8, 1998.

Sternberg, Steve. "Laptop-to-Laptop, On the Lookout for Germ Warfare." *USA Today,* September 20, 1999, 6D.

Stone, Andrea. "United States is Open to Attacks by Terrorists, Report Warns." *USA Today,* July 9, 1999, 11A.

Stoutland, Page. "Research and Development Support to Domestic Emergency Preparedness for Response to Threats of Terrorist Use of Weapons of Mass Destruction." Statement before the Military Research and Development Subcommittee of the House Armed Services Committee, March 11, 1999. Available online at <http://www.cbnp.anl.gov/Testimony.html>.

Taubman, Philip. "An Arsenal of Germs." *The New York Times Book Review,* June 20, 1999.

Taylor, J. "Sara Lee Weighed Value of Brand Names Versus Safety in Recall Decision." Knight-Ridder Tribune Business News, August 25, 1999.

Taylor, Robert. "All Fall Down." *New Scientist* 150, no. 2029 (May 11, 1996): 32–37.

Taylor, Scott R., Amy M. Rowe, and Brian M. Lewis. "Consequence Management—In Need of a Timeout." *Joint Force Quarterly* 22 (Summer 1999): 78–85.

"Terror Risk to Food Supply Seen." *The Philadelphia Inquirer,* October 28, 1999.

"Terrorism 2000." *Current Events* 97, no. 24 (1998): 2a–2d.

"Terrorists on the Green." *Discover* 20, no. 11 (1999): 30.

"The Real Threat of Bioterrorism Discussed in Atlanta." *The Lancet* 351, no. 9106 (March 21, 1998): 887.

Tritak, John S. Untitled statement by John S. Tritak, Director, Critical Infrastructure Assurance Office at Hearing before the United States Senate Judiciary Committee, Subcommittee on Technology, Terrorism, and Government Information, February 1, 2000.

Tucker, Jonathan B. "Bioterrorism Is the Least of Our Worries." *The New York Times,* October 16, 1999, A19.

——— . "Historical Trends Related to Bioterrorism: An Empirical Analysis." *Emerging Infectious Diseases* 5, no. 4 (July/August 1999). Available online at <http://www.cdc.gov/ncidod/EID/vol5no4/tucker.htm>.

——— . "Putting Teeth into the Biological Weapons Ban." *MIT Technology Review* 101, no. 1 (January/February 1998): 38–45.

——— . "Strengthening the BWC: Moving Toward a Compliance Protocol." *Arms Control Today* 28, no. 1 (January/February 1998): 20–27.

——— . "The Ultimate Terrorists. Review of *America's Achilles' Heel: Nuclear, Biological, and Chemical Terrorism and Covert Attack* by Richard A. Falkenrath, Robert D. Newman, and Bradley A. Thayer." *Survival* 41, no. 2 (Summer 1999): 170–172.

——— , and Amy Sands. "An Unlikely Threat." *Bulletin of the Atomic Scientists* 55, no. 4 (July 1999): 46–52.

United Agri Products, Inc. "Crop-Net. Organizations and Associations." Available online at <http://www.crop-net.com/organizations.html>.

United Nations, Food and Agriculture Organization. Meat Production, by Country: 1990 to 1998. FAO AGRISTAT database, no. 1396, Rome, Italy.

United States Animal Health Association. "United States Animal Health Association." Available online at <http://usaha.org>.

United States Department of Agriculture. "Departmental Administration: Disaster Coordination and Response." Available online at <http://www.usda.gov/da/disaster.html>.

———. Advisory Committee on Agricultural Biotechnology. Federal Register Notice 64, no. 108 (June 7, 1999): 30297.

———. Agricultural Research Service. ". . . about the Research Center at Plum Island, New York." Available online at <http://www.arserrc.gov/naa/home/piadc.htm>.

———. Agricultural Research Service. "Econoterrorism, a.k.a. Agricultural Bioterrorism or Asymmetric Use of Biological Weapons." Unclassified briefing, February 28, 2000.

———. Agricultural Research Service. "FY 2001 Agency Estimates: Enhancing the Capabilities of U.S. Agriculture to Prevent, Respond to, and Remediate Terrorist Events."

———. Animal and Plant Health Inspection Service. "Center for Animal Health Monitoring (CAHM): National Animal Health Monitoring System." Available online at <http://www.aphis.usda.gov/vs/ceah/cahm.htm>.

———. Animal and Plant Health Inspection Service. "Emergency Programs: Keeping America Free from Foreign Animal Diseases." Available online at <http://www.aphis.usda.gov/oa/emergency.html>.

———. Animal and Plant Health Inspection Service. "Facts about APHIS: Monitoring Plant and Animal Pests and Diseases." Available online at <http://www.aphis.usda.gov/oa/monitor.html>.

———. Animal and Plant Health Inspection Service. "Facts about APHIS: Excluding Foreign Pests and Diseases." Available online at <http://www.aphis.usda.gov/oa/exclude.html>.

———. Animal and Plant Health Inspection Service. "The Foreign Animal Disease Diagnostic Laboratory at Plum Island Animal Disease Center." December 1992. Available online at <http://www.aphis.usda.gov:80/oa/pubs/fsfadlab.html>.

———. Food Safety and Inspection Service. "Agriculture Fact Book 98: Chapter 9. Food Safety." Available online at <http://www.usda.gov/news/pubs/fbook98/chart9.htm>.

————. Foreign Agricultural Service. "Selected Farm Products—United States and World Production and Exports: 1995 to 1998." Foreign Agricultural Commodity Circular Series, no. 1124.

————. National Agricultural Statistics Service. "Agriculture—Farms, Acreage, Income, and Foreign Trade: 1990 to 1998," no. 1441.

United States Department of Health and Human Services. Office of Emergency Preparedness. "States Receive $40 Million for Strong Public Health Preparedness for Bioterrorism." *M2 Presswire*, September 16, 1999.

United States Department of Justice. "Report to Congress on the Extent of Domestic and International Terrorism in Animal Enterprises," September 2, 1993.

United States Department of State. United States Information Agency. "NSC's Berger: 'Last Weeks of 1999 Saw Largest U.S. Counter-Terrorism Operation in History.'" *Washington File*, January 6, 2000. Available online at <http://www.usia.gov/topical/pol/terror/00010601.htm>.

————. United States Information Agency. "Response to Terrorism." Available online at <http://www.usia.gov/topical/pol/terror>.

United States House of Representatives. 104th Congress, 2d Session. Effective Death Penalty and Public Safety Act of 1996, S. 735 (March 14, 1996).

————. "The Threat of Bioterrorism in America: Assessing the Adequacy of the Federal Law Relating to Dangerous Biological Agents." Hearing before the Subcommittee on Oversight and Investigations of the Committee on Commerce (May 20, 1999).

United States Senate. Committee on Appropriations, Subcommittee on Labor, Health, and Human Services, and Education, and Related Agencies. Special Hearing, "Preparedness for Epidemics and Bioterrorism" (June 2, 1998).

————. 105th Congress, 2d Session. Senate Record Vote Analysis: Agriculture Appropriations/Food-Medicine Sanctions and Terrorism. July 15, 1998. P. S. 8227, Temp. Record. Vote No. 204.

————. Agriculture Appropriations/Food-Medicine Sanctions and Terrorism. Agriculture, Rural Development, and Related Agencies Appropriations Bill for Fiscal Year 1999 . . . S.2159. Dodd motion to table the Torricelli Amendment No. 3160 to the Dodd Amendment No. 3158, as amended.

"USA Extends NBC Training to Civilian Contractors." *Jane's Defence Weekly*, April 15, 1998, 11.

U.S. Bureau of Economic Analysis. "Gross Domestic Product in Current and Real (1992) Dollars, by Industry: 1990 to 1997." *Survey of Current Business*, no. 722 (November 1998).

"U.S. Could Face New Terror Tactic: Agricultural Warfare." *The Philadelphia Inquirer*, June 22, 1999.

"U.S. Military Wants No Domestic Law-Enforcement Role." *USA Today*, October 5, 1999, 16A.

U.S. National Response Team. "Ensuring Effective National Oil and Hazardous Substances Preparedness and Response." Available online at <http://www.nrt.org>.

"Vaccine Experts Report Progress Against Bioterrorism, Cancer." *PR Newswire* (March 26, 1999).

Van Peursem, Denise R. Issue Paper submitted to the U.S. House of Representatives Agriculture Subcommittee on Risk Management, Research, and Specialty Crops (March 10, 1999).

VanderMeer, Dan C. "The Threat of Things Biological." *Environmental Health Perspectives* 106, no. 6 (June 1998): A280–A282.

Vegar, Jose. "Terrorism's New Breed." *Bulletin of the Atomic Scientists* 54, no. 2 (March/April 1998): 50–55.

Venter, Al J. "Biological Warfare: The Poor Man's Atomic Bomb." *Jane's Intelligence Review* 11, no. 3 (March 1, 1999): 42–47.

———."Elements Loyal to Bin Laden Acquire Biological Agents 'Through the Mail.'" *Jane's Intelligence Review* 11, no. 8 (August 1, 1999): 1.

———."Keeping the Lid on Germ Warfare." *Jane's International Defence Review* (May 1, 1998): 26–32.

———."New-Era Threat: Iraq's Biological Weapons." *Middle East Policy* 6, no. 4 (June 1999): 104–117.

———."Spectre of Biowar Remains." *Jane's Defence Weekly* 31, no. 17 (April 28, 1999): 1–4.

Voelker, Rebecca. "Disease Tracking—And More." *JAMA* 280, no. 2 (July 8, 1998): 125.

Vogel, Steve. "High-Profile Marine Unit Moving Here; Terrorist Response Team Repositioning Near Capital." *The Washington Post,* January 8, 2000, B1.

Volland, Craig G. "The Threat to the Food Supply Starts at Home." *The New York Times,* September 28, 1999, A24.

Wadman, Meredith. "Action Needed To Counter Bioterrorism." *Nature* 388, no. 6644 (August 21, 1997): 703.

Walterscheid, Ellen. "Ill Wind." *Science* 38, no. 2 (March/April 1998): 10–11.

Waxman, Dov. "Terrorism: The War of the Future." *The Fletcher Forum of World Affairs* 23, no. 2 (Fall 1999): 201–208.

Weiner, Tim. "Reno Says U.S. May Stockpile Medicine for Terrorist Attacks." *The New York Times,* April 23, 1998, A14.

Whitby, Simon, and Paul Rogers. "Anti-Crop Biological Warfare—Implications of the Iraqi and U.S. Programs." *Defense Analysis* 13, no. 3 (December 1997): 303–318.

White House. Fact Sheet: Combating Terrorism: Presidential Decision Directive 62. May 22, 1998. Available online at <http://www.nbcindustrygroup.com/0522pres3.htm>.

————. Fact Sheet: Preparedness for a Biological Weapons Attack. May 22, 1998. Available online at <http://www.nbcindustrygroup.com/0522pres1.htm>.

————. Fact Sheet: Keeping America Secure for the 21st Century: President Clinton's Initiative on Biological and Chemical Weapons Preparedness. Available online at <http://www.pub.whitehouse.gov/uri-res/I2Rurn:pdi://oma.eop.gov.us/1999/1/22/8.text.1>.

————. *A National Security Strategy for a New Century.* December 1999.

————. President and Vice President's FY 2000 Budget—Preparing America for the 21st Century. February 2, 1999.

————. The White House: Preserving America's privacy and security in the next century. *M2 Presswire,* September 17, 1999.

————. White Paper: The Clinton Administration's Policy on Critical Infrastructure Protection: Presidential Decision Directive 63, May 22, 1998.

————. White Paper: The Clinton Administration's Policy on International Public Information: Presidential Decision Directive 68, April 1999.

————. White Paper: The Clinton Administration's Policy on Managing Complex Contingency Operations: Presidential Decision Directive 56, May 1997.

Whittaker, A. "Update on NSC Structure and Operations." Undated Memorandum to Political Science Faculty, Industrial College of the Armed Forces, National Defense University, 1999.

Wiant, Chris J. "Biological Weapons: What Role Should Environmental Health Specialists Take in Protecting Our Communities?" *Journal of Environmental Health* 60, no. 9 (May 1998): 25, 65.

Wild, J.R. "Enzymatic Based Detection and Decontamination of Pesticide Contaminated Soils and Water." Texas A&M University, Biochemistry and Biophysics Research Project Report, Project No. 0098214 (1998).

Wildavsky, Rachel. "Are We Ready for Terror?" *Reader's Digest* 154, no. 921 (January 1999): 84–91.

————. "Coming Soon: The Next Great Flu Epidemic." *Reader's Digest* 155, no. 931 (November 1999): 114–119.

Wilson, D., and Randall S. Murch. "Scientific Investigation of Bioterrorism: FBI Laboratory Viewpoint." Abstracts of the 1999 American Phytopathological Society Annual Meeting Symposium: Plant Pathology's Role in Anti-Crop Bioterrorism and Food Security (September 15–October 31, 1999).

Wilson, Terrance M., et al. "A Review of Agroterrorism, Biological Crimes, and Biological Warfare Targeting Animal Agriculture." Draft manuscript.

Wise, Richard. "Bioterrorism: Thinking the Unthinkable." *The Lancet* 351, no. 9113 (May 9, 1998): 1378.

Wolfe, Frank. "Army Bio Detection Platoon Deployed for First Time." *Defense Daily* 198, no. 41 (March 4, 1998): 1.

Woodall, Jack. "Stalking the Next Epidemic: ProMED Tracks Emerging Diseases." *Public Health Reports* 112 (January/February 1997): 78–82.

Wright, Evelyn L. "Taking AIM at the Nightmare Bug." *Business Week* (November 1, 1999): 78.

Zakaria, Tabassum. "Soviet Era Bugs Threaten U.S. Farming." *The Times of India,* September 16, 1999.

Zilinskas, Raymond A. "Bioethics and Biological Weapons." *Science* 279, no. 5351 (January 30, 1998): 635.

————. "Iraq's Biological Weapons: The Past as Future?" *JAMA* 278, no. 5 (August 6, 1997): 418–424.

Zoon, Kathryn C. "Vaccines, Pharmaceutical Products, and Bioterrorism: Challenges for the U.S. Food and Drug Administration." *Emerging Infectious Diseases* 5, no. 4 (July/August 1999). Available online at <http://www.cdc.gov/ncidod/EID/vol5no4/zoon/htm>.